A Magna Colour Guide

FISHES
OF LAKES AND RIVERS

A Magna Colour Guide

FISHES
OF LAKES AND RIVERS

by
KAREL PECL

Illustrated by
JIŘÍ MALÝ & KVĚTOSLAV HÍSEK

MAGNA BOOKS

Text by Karel Pecl
Illustrations by Jiří Malý and Květoslav Hísek
Translated by Clare and Jiří Krojzl
Graphic design by Eva Adamcová

This edition published 1995 by Magna Books
Magna Road, Wigston
Leicester LE18 4ZH, and produced in co-operation with
Arcturus Publishing Limited

ISBN 1-85422-844-7
Printed in Slovakia by Neografia, Martin
3/15/26/51-02

CONTENTS

INTRODUCTION

Water. The amount that has already been written about this liquid! It is the cradle of all life on Earth. It covers 75 per cent of the Earth's surface. It is a medium both of transport and of communication. It forms 60—90 per cent of animal's bodies and is as essential and indispensible to life as food. It is also the natural environment for a large number of living creatures. Within that most aquatic of groups, the fishes, there are almost 20,000 species living in the waters of the world, and approximately one quarter of these live in fresh water.

There is, however, *water* and *water.* Over the area of 10.5 million sq. km. comprising the continent of Europe there is a whole range of water types. Flowing water comes in many forms. We can find cool, swift mountain torrents, slowly-flowing little lowland brooks, swift, wild, submontane rivers full of rapids and the wide lazily-flowing rivers of the lowlands. Amongst still water-bodies we find the cold, emerald-green eyes of glacial mountain lakes, the extensive, deep waters of dam reservoirs, the shallow, muddy and overgrown waters of ponds, small densely overgrown pools, lakes in abandoned quarries, oxbow lakes, reclamation canals, marshes, lagoons and lakes in river estuaries with both fresh and brackish water, coastal lakes with brackish water and finally the coastal parts of seas in the vicinity of river estuaries.

Many mysteries are concealed under the surface of these waters. In this book we have tried to reveal at least some of these and to acquaint the reader with the European representatives of Cyclostomata (roundmouths) and fishes. We have not restricted ourselves to purely freshwater species, but have also included brackish water species. Also included are those which penetrate brackish and fresh waters only for a time, for example to spawn or in search of food. Within this broader definition of European waters there are 215 extant fish species belonging to 29 families. Of these, 157 species from 27 families have been selected for this book.

WATER AS A LIVING ENVIRONMENT

Fresh waters cover an area of 2.5 million sq. km. on the Earth's surface, which represents 1.7 per cent of the dry land surface. Roughly 5,000 fish species live in these waters, although obviously they do not all coexist in the same habitats! Some fish species are very adaptable and can live in many types of environment, for example the Chub.

Other species, however, have very precise habitat requirements and even then only occur in small numbers in a restricted area. A good example of this strategy is the Mudminnow.

The occurrence of certain species is influenced not only by the type of water, but also by its quality, which is determined by its mineral content, water temperature, oxygen content, its pH and the currents, depth and size of the environment.

The amount of dissolved minerals and salts determines the density of the water. The differences between the density of fresh and salt water are so great that they have become an insuperable obstacle for many fish species. Nevertheless, there are fishes which can prosper in salt water and in the brackish water of river estuaries and bays in the vicinity of these estuaries. And there are even species which will at any time swim from the sea into rivers and vice versa (for example the Gudgeon or the Three-spined Stickleback). Most fish species, however, remain true either to fresh or salt water.

Different fish species show a variety of tolerances and requirements with regard to water temperature, which in turn is influenced by altitude and geographical latitude. Trout and the Burbot are good examples of cool-loving fishes. Waters whose summer temperatures do not exceed 15 °C suit the Brown Trout (*Salmo trutta* m. *fario*). When the temperature reaches 18 °C it stops feeding, and it reproduces at a temperature of around 4 °C. The Burbot likewise spawns in winter, at which time it is also most active and most voracious. In summer, when temperatures are higher, it falls into a state of rest, the so-called aestivation. Catfish and Tench overcome the summer heat in a similar manner.

The opposite of cool-loving fishes are the thermophilic fishes. Carp thrive at a temperature of 22—25 °C, which is a deadly temperature for trout. When the temperature drops below 8 °C, Carp stop feeding and survive the winter without food in a state of rest with sloweddown heart activity and respiration. Most carp-type or cyprinid fishes, as well as many other fish species, hibernate when temperatures drop to 4—6 °C. The most extreme example of a thermophilic fish is a rudd subspecies — *Scardinius erythrophthalmus racovitzai,* which inhabits hot springs in Romania with a temperature of 28—34 °C! It perishes if the temperature drops below 20 °C.

Most European freshwater fishes adapt relatively easily to the temperature of the environment. The greatest temperature range can be withstood by a species imported from the USA — the Mosquito Fish (*Gambusia affinis*). It inhabits waters with a temperature ranging from 0.3 °C to 34 °C.

The most important gas dissolved in water is oxygen. The oxygen content changes according to temperature as does its consumption by living organisms. In some types of water there is so little oxygen that fishes cannot live there at all. In other waters, however, its level decreases only during certain seasons, usually the summer. A temporary drop in the oxygen level is dealt with by fishes in various ways. The Weatherfish swallows air from the water surface; it reaches the rear section of the gut, where it is absorbed into the bloodstream. The Tench solves the problem by absorbing oxygen via the skin. The Crucian Carp can produce energy from the body's reserves (so-called anaerobic respiration) and is best off in this respect. Thanks to this, it can survive for up to six months in the damp environment of the bottom with limited oxygen. The acidity or alkalinity of water (pH) depends upon its origins and its surroundings. Waters which percolate through chalk or limestone are usually alkaline, while waters from peat regions are acid. Most water is slightly acid and as a result of atmospheric pollution by sulphur dioxide this acidity is constantly increasing. Fishes can usually tolerate slight changes in acidity, higher acidity (that is lower pH) causing retarded growth and a reduction in size. Substantial changes in pH can be withstood by only a few species such as the Crucian Carp and the Roach. In highly acidic peat waters, only the Brook Trout, the Mudminnow, Pike-perch, Crucian Carp and perhaps the Tench and Roach will survive.

With regard to the other qualitative factors — currents and the depth and size of the environment — the water currents are of the greatest significance. In still waters the level of the water flow is nil, while waters with a one-way current are termed flowing waters. Flowing waters are further divided according to the swiftness of the current into four zones. The individual zones have been named after the most typical fish species found there. The trout zone is situated in mountain and submontane brooks and streams. It is characterized by cool water with a high oxygen content, a swift current, rapids, waterfalls and deeper pools. The bottom is either sandy or gravelly with an abundance of potential hiding places. Apart from the Brown Trout, this belt is also inhabited by the Alpine Bullhead, Miller's Thumb, Brook Charr, Minnow, Loach, Goby, Dace and in deeper places also the Barbel, Eelpout and Chub. The exact species make-up in any stream is determined by its geographical position. In the lower part of the zone the Lampern, Grayling and Huchen may penetrate during spawning. Pike and Perch may rarely appear in pools on the margin between the trout zone and the grayling zone which follows.

As we follow the brook's progress downstream we come to the

grayling zone. It is characterised by somewhat greater depth, slower currents and warmer water. Typical fishes for this zone are the Grayling, Goby, Nase, Loach, Riffle Minnow, Rainbow Trout, Huchen and Dace. The Brown Trout, Brook Charr, Miller's Thumb and Minnow sometimes penetrate from the trout zone, whereas Barbel and Chub sometimes swim there from the lower reaches.

Descending to lower elevations we reach the barbel zone, this being formed by deeper and larger rivers, in which shallow, swifter reaches with a stony bottom alternate with calmer and deeper places with a sandy bottom. In swifter sections live the Barbel, Nase, Loach, Alburn and Goby, while the occurrence of Miller's Thumb declines. In calmer, deeper reaches one can encounter the Roach and in the most downstream parts of the barbel zone Pike-perch, Ruffe, Bream, Pike, Asp, Dace, and Eel may occur.

The last lowland section is the bream zone. Apart from several species of bream, one can also find Carp, Catfish, Eel, Pike, Orfe, Chub, Alburn, Gudgeon, Pike-perch and Sturgeon. Tench, Rudd, Weatherfish, Bitterling, Sunbleak, Roach and Crucian Carps are found in old river arms. During the winter, Barbel and Ruffe may descend into the bream zone to a more hospitable climate. These four arbitrary zones of a river are, necessarily, only a *rough* guide to the regions of a typical European river. The margins between zones are not clear-cut and there is a lot of species-overlap between them. Man has influenced most European rivers to a greater or lesser extent. In some places the courses of whole rivers have been changed. Elsewhere, dams and weirs alter the water flow and many atypical fish species have been introduced.

Not all the zones are necessarily found in every river. Some zones, on the other hand, can occur in a single course two or more times, for example when a dam is constructed in the trout zone. Where copious tributaries slow down the current and warm the water, this can change into a bream zone. Because Man often changes the natural character of river courses and pollutes them, consequently he can also change the species composition in an individual zone. Thus today, for example, in many places in Europe the typical species — the Grayling — has disappeared from the grayling zone.

Fishes also inhabit most purpose-built canals. The living conditions are affected by the construction and living of the canal and by its function. As long as canals link up with natural river courses or still waters, species from these environments will penetrate them. In larger canals Roach, Tench, Weatherfish, Pike and Crucian Carp occur. Canals frequently become overgrown with aquatic plants, their navigability thus being reduced. In order to clear the waterway, herbivorous fish species are sometimes brought in, chiefly the introduced Grass Carp. More often, however, the canals are dredged mechanically.

Waters which permanently lack any flow are termed still waters. These are represented by many types, of which only a few can be considered natural. Examples include lakes of glacial and volcanic origin, as well as waters formed in folds and faults in the Earth's crust. Many other still waters are a result of human activity, among them for example lakes left behind after gravel and sand quarrying, flooded quarries and surface mines, some ponds and purpose-built irrigation reservoirs. Valley reservoirs for electricity generation or supplying towns with drinking water represent a certain intermediary stage between flowing and still waters.

In some man-made environments, conditions are so favourable for fish that they grow faster there and reach a greater size than they would under natural conditions. This applies above all to some valley reservoirs. The construction of new types of water environment, together with planned fishing management, could help to conserve the wealth of fish species in European waters. The establishment of new species is considered by some to increase this wealth.

Many factors, however, adversely affect fish populations. The alternation of natural courses, river canalisation, but above all the pollution of all waters, is leading to a reduction both in the numbers and richness of fish species in Europe. Sadly, this theme runs through all the text dealing with individual species.

MORPHOLOGY OF THE FISH BODY AND ITS SURFACE

The shape of a fish's body has evolved to suit its mode of life and the particular environment in which the respective species occurs. Water density has been a great influence in this evolution since it is 775 times denser than air and its resistance is roughly 100 times higher. Fishes reduce the effect of water resistance not only by their streamlined body-shape, but also by its smoothness. The need to minimise resistance has led, during the course of fish evolution, to still further adaptations. In the case of fast swimmers there are no non-functional protuberances on the body. The opercula are pressed firmly to the body, the eyes are in sockets, not protruding beyond the body contour, and even the paired fins, which have no use in fast swimming, are lodged in precisely shaped depressions in the body. The torpedo-like shape can be found in the majority of fast open-sea fishes, and from among freshwater fishes in the trout, salmon, Huchen, Dace and Mullet.

The diversity of freshwater environments has led to the evolution of other types of fish body. The arrow-like shape of a Pike's body is similar to the torpedo-like shape, the difference between these being in the position of the non-paired fins. These lie more towards the caudal fin, a larger surface area being created in the tail section. This enables the fish to make a sudden thrust from a resting position. Territorial predatory species which hunt by attacking from an ambush are equipped with this body shape. If they miss, they do not usually pursue their quarry further. The pike-like shape is also found in the Mudminnow and the marine pipefishes.

The most frequent body form in freshwater fishes is the flat-sided, discoid shape. It can be found in fishes of the open waters (pelagic), such as for example Bream, and in bottom-dwelling (benthic) fishes, such as the Plaice. Benthic fishes have flat-sided bodies like the breams, but lie only on one side on the bottom. In fresh waters, this body shape occurs only in the Flounder and Dover Sole.

The last, highly specialized type is the eel-like shape. This differs greatly from the classic concept of the fish body, being more reminiscent of the body of a snake. Apart from the Eel, lamperns and hagfish, traces of this shape can also be found for example in the Loach or Weatherfish. The above-mentioned types are only the extremes.

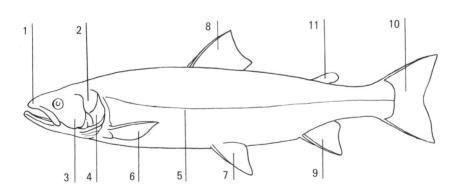

Fig. 1. The fish body:
1—head, 2, 3, 4—operculum bones, 5—lateral line, 6—pectoral fin, 7—ventral fin, 8—dorsal fin, 9—anal fin, 10—caudal fin, 11—adipose fin

There is also a whole range of intermediary stages determined by the specific requirement of a particular environment.

A fish's body can be divided into the head, trunk and tail (Fig. 1). In cartilaginous fishes the head is bounded by the anterior margin of the first gill slit, and in bony fishes by the posterior margin of the operculum. The trunk terminates at the anal orifice, where the tail begins. The head begins at the mouth. The eyes are lidless and their size is to a certain extent dependent on the mode of life. The lateral line often ends on the head and then in most fishes continues along the middle of the side of the body as far as the tail.

One of the most characteristic features of fish are the fins. There are paired pectoral and ventral fins and non-paired dorsal and anal fins. It is a popular misconception that the paired fins are essential for locomotion of the fish, like oars for a boat. Instead, the paired fins control the direction of motion, while the tail-end, and in particular the caudal fin, supply the power for locomotion. The paired fins ensure a horizontal position in a state of rest, and in motion they serve both to maintain the horizontal position or aid directional control when swimming upwards or downwards. The dorsal and anal fins are also used in directional control, assist the fish when it is submerging and rising to the surface and direct the stream of water towards the caudal fin.

A whole range of forms has evolved from the basic paired and non-paired fins. For example, the Salmon, Grayling, Cisco and Pout families possess an additional small adipose fin between the dorsal and caudal fins. In some families, the dorsal fin consists of two parts, which are either connected (as in case of the Centrarchidae family), or separate (as in case of the Perch and Cod families). In eels the ventral fins are absent and the unpaired fins are connected into a single long one. In case of the Goby family, the ventral fins are modified to form a sucker with which the fish clings to stones at the bottom. As you

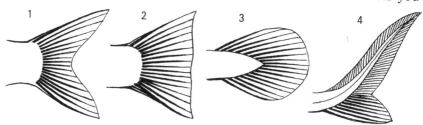

Fig. 2. Caudal fin shapes:
1—fin indented with symmetrical tail lobes, 2—straight-edged fin, 3—fin symmetrical both inside and out, 4—asymmetrical fin

12

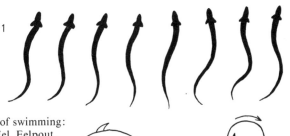

Fig. 3. Two basic methods of swimming:
1—snake-like movement (Eel, Eelpout,
Lamprey), 2—movement starting from
tail end of body

2

can see there are many forms of adaptation, almost as many adaptations as there are fish species.

The tail section of a fish begins behind the anal orifice, usually terminating at the end in a powerful caudal fin (Fig. 2). The caudal fin is not uniform in all roundmouths and fishes. During the course of evolution, three types have developed, differing both in appearance and in anatomical structure. In the majority of fishes, the fin appears approximately symmetrical (homocercous). Its inner structure, however, is not usually symmetrical, because the vertebrae at the end of the spine turn upwards at the base of the caudal fin. Homocercous caudal fins are usually indented with symmetrical caudal lobes. Lampreys, on the other hand, have a fin which is symmetrical both in appearance and in structure (diphycercous). In sturgeons, the caudal fin is asymmetrical (heterocercous), and here the terminal part of the spine protrudes into the upper lobe of the caudal fin. The position, length and shape of the fins are an important systematic feature.

The body shape and position of the fins affect the method and speed of swimming (Fig. 3). In spite of the wide variety of body and fin shapes and fin positions, two basic methods of swimming can be distinguished. Fishes with an eel-like body shape (Eel, Lampern, Loach, Weatherfish, Catfish and Burbot), swim with a snake-like motion, in which the greater proportion of the body is engaged in an undulating motion. In other fish species, the motion starts from the tail section of the body.

Lastly, we cannot omit one more special feature of the fish body, namely the scales (Fig. 4). Scales are thin, bony plates about a quarter of which is embedded in the skin. The free parts overlap one another

13

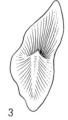

Fig. 4. Types of fish scale:
1—cycloid scale, 2—ctenoid scale,
3—body plate of Acipenseridae   1   2   3

like roof tiles and serve the same protective function as the chainmail of a medieval knight. They protect the delicate skin from injury and at the same time do not hinder either movement or the other functions of the skin.

In true fishes, two types of scales have formed during evolution. The Carp and Salmon families, for example, have rounded, smooth-surfaced *cycloid* scales, whereas fishes of the Perch family have square, rough-surfaced *ctenoid* scales. In the case of the primitive Sturgeon family, the skin is protected by bony plates, which are either connected to one another, as on the head, or form rows on the back, sides and belly. Smaller bony plates are freely dispersed in the skin. These free plates can also be found in some bony fishes, for example in the Goby (*Benthophilus macrocephalus*), or in the Fourhorn Sculpin (*Myoxocephalus quadricornis*). Both types of scales as well as the bony plates can be found on the body of the Flounder.

WHAT IS CONCEALED
UNDER THE BODY SURFACE?

The skeleton of lampreys and sturgeon is cartilaginous and thus differs from the skeleton of bony fishes (Fig. 5). The skeleton of bony fishes is divided into the vertebral column, skull and fin skeleton. The vertebral column forms the body axis. Whereas mammals mostly have 32 vertebrae, fishes have 40—80 and the Eel up to 200. On the sides the musculature is attached to the ribs and vertebral spines. This facilitates side movements of the body, a precondition for swimming. The most powerful musculature is to be found in the dorsal section. Apart from the true ribs, fishes are additionally equipped with false intermuscular ribs. These are the tiny Y-shaped bones which cause difficulties when eating fish. The skeleton of the pectoral fins is firmly attached to the bones of the head, and the skeleton of the cau-

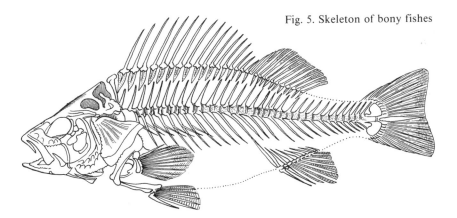

Fig. 5. Skeleton of bony fishes

dal fin to the vertebral column. The bones of the other fins are freely anchored in the musculature.

The swim-bladder occurs exclusively in fishes. By virtue of this organ they can remain effortlessly in the water column at precise depths. By transferring gases from the blood, the swim-bladder becomes enlarged and the fish swims near the surface. When the fish dives downwards, gas is absorbed from the bladder into the blood, the bladder shrinks and the fish has no difficulty moving at greater depths. By means of this exchange of gases between the blood and swim-bladder, the fish regulates its specific gravity and thus compensates for the pressure of the surrounding water.

The shape of the swim-bladder and its connection with the digestive system varies in the different families (Fig. 6). In the Pike family,

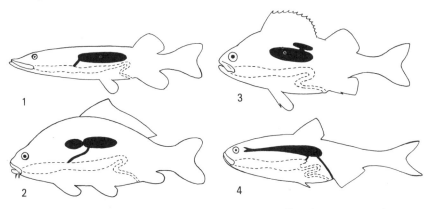

Fig. 6. Swim bladder shapes and its connection with the digestive system: 1—in Esocidae, 2—in Cyprinidae, 3—in Percidae, 4—in Clupeidae

15

the swim-bladder is elongated and the front part is connected with the gullet. In fishes of the Carp family there is also a connection with the gullet, but only in the second part of the two-chamber bladder. The transfer of gases to the front or rear chamber enables fishes of the Carp family to remain stationary in water with the head pointing either upwards or downwards. They are thus able to gather food both from the bottom and the surface. Fishes of the Perch family also have a two-chamber swim-bladder, but the smaller chamber lies over the larger one and there is no connection with the gullet. In the case of fishes which dive to greater depths, for example in members of the Herring family, the swim-bladder is linked both with the gullet and with the outside environment. When the fish descends to the depths, the increasing water pressure forces gas out of the bladder, which enables it to dive without difficulties or damaging its body.

The basic supply of gas reaches the swim-bladder from the outer environment during the larval development stage. Perches thus have the swim-bladder connected with the gullet during the larval development stage. This connection disappears during later development. This filling of the swim-bladder takes place several days after the alevins hatch. If they are prevented from reaching the surface during this critical period, the gas supply in the swim-bladder is incomplete and this organ cannot fulfil its function correctly. In bottom-dwelling species such as bullheads and gobies, the swim-bladder has either completely disappeared or is substantially reduced.

The main organs of respiration in fishes are the gills (Fig. 7). These

Fig. 7. The gills are the main organ of respiration:
1—gill arch, 2—gill-rakers, 3—gill lamellae

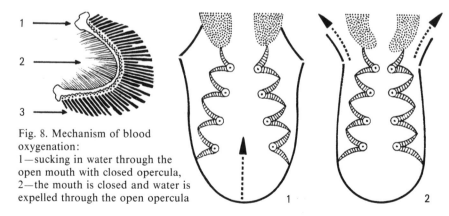

1

2

3

Fig. 8. Mechanism of blood oxygenation:
1—sucking in water through the open mouth with closed opercula,
2—the mouth is closed and water is expelled through the open opercula

1

2

16

are situated in the oral cavity, and on the outer surface, under the opercula, there are gill lamellae. The gill arches thus fulfil a dual function. The gill septa catch and filter food and the gill lamellae transfer oxygen from the water to the blood.

Oxygenation of the blood (Fig. 8) occurs when water passes over the gills. Initially water is taken in through the open mouth with the opercula closed and then the mouth is closed and water is expelled through the open opercula. This ensures a one-way flow over the gills. Besides this basic gill respiration mechanism, fishes have other ways of overcoming periods of temporary oxygen deficiency, which occur mainly in the summer. With an increase in temperature from 5 °C to 30 °C, the oxygen content of the water drops to half. The oxygen reduction is particularly harmful in waters where the content was relatively low in the first place. Fish which live in still and muddy waters are particularly at risk. The Weatherfish has intestinal auxiliary respiration, the Mudminnow utilises its swim-bladder for respiration, the Tench uses its skin, and the Crucian Carp produces oxygen from its reserve substances.

INFORMATION SYSTEMS

In addition to vision, hearing, touch, smell and taste, fishes have another exclusively fish sense. They can detect minute changes in water pressure caused by objects in the surrounding environment and the seat of this sense is the organ known as the lateral line (Fig. 9). In most species, this remarkable organ runs along the side of the body, hence its name. However, in some fish species it does not occur on the sides of the body at all, but is concentrated only on the head. When a fish swims it drives the water ahead of it. The pressure wave reflects off obstacles and returns to the fish as a reflectory wave, being perceived by the fish with the lateral line (Fig. 10). By this means it can avoid obstacles or register food and predators, even for example in muddy waters or complete darkness where sight itself alone would be useless. Fish also maintain constant contact within the shoal with the aid of the lateral line.

Another important sense of orientation is vision. The fish eye has a somewhat different structure from the mammalian eye. Focusing does not occur by means of the flattening and rounding of the eye lens as in mammals, but by the shifting of the lens, which has a constant shape, either towards the retina or away from it. A light-sensitive retinal layer is formed by cells of the same type as in Man, that is

17

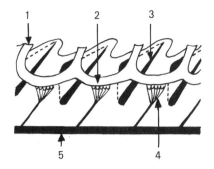

Fig. 9. The lateral line is a system of pores (1) linked together by a network of small canals (2) which are situated just under the surface of the body along the sides and on the head. The pores on the body pass through the scales (3). Behind the pores there are sensory cells (4), the terminations of which are conducted to a nerve (5), through which information is carried to the brain

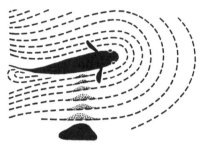

Fig. 10. When moving the fish drives water in front of itself, a pressure wave reflecting from obstacles and returning to the fish as a reflector wave, which is registered by the fish via the lateral line

by both rods and cones. Fishes are, therefore, also able to see in colour. This ability is reflected in the colourfulness of fish bodies, their ability to change colour during the reproductive period, as well as by colour difference between the sexes. Fish species inhabiting clear waters in particular, where sight is of major importance, are often conspicuously coloured to our eyes. However, the bright colours generally have a deceptive function, allowing the fish to blend in with its surroundings. Fish species of deeper waters, on the other hand, often have a more or less drab appearance, the back being darker, the sides lighter, and the belly the lightest. Most cyprinid fish species, for example, have this colouring. Seen from above, the dark back merges with the surrounding dark water. When seen from the side, the fish's colour matches the surrounding water. Seen from below, that is against the light, the fish is again perfectly masked by the light colouring of its belly.

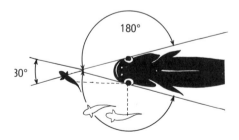

Fig. 11. Most fishes have the eyes situated on the sides of the head

Fig. 12. A fish can see a fisherman even if he stands quite far from the water. A shy fish then hides even as he arrives, so that the fisherman waits for a catch in vain

Most fishes have their eyes on the sides of the head (Fig. 11). This positioning is suitable for fishes which are prey species. They are able to detect a dangerous predator over a wide area. For predators, on the other hand, the lateral positioning of the eyes is unsuitable. The angle in which a predatory fish can see its quarry with both eyes is only 30°. The predator must frame the quarry into this relatively small sector in front of its mouth, in order to be able to judge its distance accurately and to attack it successfully.

The difference between the densities of water and air is the reason why light rays are refracted at the interface between these two mediums, and why the angle of vision is greater in air than in water. This fact puts the fisherman at an immediate disadvantage, because a fish can see him even when he is standing quite far away from the water (Fig. 12).

The sense of smell is very fine and is situated in paired olfactory pits on the snout in front of the eyes. The simple pit is in some species covered over with a fold of skin, which divides the pit into two parts evaginating on the surface at two apertures. Through the first of these, closer to the snout, water flows into the pit, flowing out through the second, rear one. In the case of bullheads, the Eel, Eelpout and other species, the nostrils are tube-like and protrude above the surface of the head.

The organ of hearing in fishes is located inside the head and is connected with the organ of balance. The 'ear' does not open to the outside via an auditory canal as in terrestrial vertebrates, the reason for this being the different properties of water as the medium carrying the sound. Since the fish's body contains a large quantity of water, the body fluids participate in the transfer of sound from the surrounding water to the ear. In many species, mainly freshwater ones, the hearing system is linked with the swim-bladder, which further amplifies sounds.

19

For many of us, the water environment is connected with the concept of 'the world of silence'. If we submerge under the surface, however, this concept at once disappears. Like fish, we can hear the splashing of hunting predators, the smacking sounds of carp when swallowing food, and the creaking noise they make when crushing mollusc shells with their gullet teeth. One is at once convinced that fish can not only hear but also produce sounds. The Weatherfish smacks when swallowing air from the surface and whistles when expelling air through its anus. The Catfish growls and drums with the aid of the swim-bladder. Perhaps this is the fish's way of finding a prospective partner.

The exact location of the organs of taste in fish is still unknown. At first the ability of fish to taste was denied by many. Experiments have shown, however, that fishes, like Man, are able to perceive four basic tastes. Taste cells have been demonstrated in the mouth and its vicinity. In some species, however, they are also to be found on the outside of the head and on the body epidermis. The sensory barbels which some fish possess may also play a part in tasting both the environment and food.

With their sense of taste and smell fishes are able to perceive the chemical composition of water. This fact is of fundamental importance in the case of migrating species, for example salmons, which in order to reproduce seek out the river in which they themselves were spawned. The discerning ability of both the taste and olfactory cells of these fish is so great that they can find their native river even over enormous distances.

EATING IS A MUST

Fish spend most of their lives feeding. Most of them are carnivorous, devouring small living creatures, with larger predators hunting other fish. Food is distributed throughout the whole water column and the bottom, so different species have adapted in many ways to the variety of sites and sources of food.

Let us first take a look at the bottom: here live insect larvae, molluscs and worms, while algae and aquatic plants also grow here. The animal life of the bottom (benthos) is gathered, for example, by the Bullhead, which seeks out predominantly animals concealed under stones. Snake-like loaches, on the other hand, gather food between stones, and from the bottom sediments food is gathered by the protrusible mouths of the Carp and Common Bream. Before swallowing it, they crush and filter it with their false, so-called pharyngeal teeth. Indigestible parts of food are spat out back on to the bottom. The Nase also looks on the bottom for its food, this consisting mainly of algae, which it scrapes off with its hard, sharp-edged lower jaw. Characteristic tracks are left behind on the stones where it has grazed on plant cover. Mullets also graze aquatic plants in a similar manner. In spite of the fact that both Nase and Mullets live mainly on a plant diet, they nevertheless inadvertently swallow many small animals. Compared to carnivorous species, herbivorous fishes require both more time and a larger gut to process the resistant cellulose of plant bodies.

Minute plant and animal organisms (phytoplankton and zooplankton) are present in open water. The fishes which live on these are planktonivorous. Ciscos, for example, filter zooplankton from the water through a filtering apparatus formed by the dense long gill-rakers on the inner side of the gill arches. Phytoplankton is filtered from the water by the Silver Carp, while the related Big Head Carp makes use of both types of planktonic food. Larger, predatory species live on alevins or smaller fish species. In open water the cyprinid Asp hunts its smaller non-predatory relative. The lightning-fast Huchen hunts in small submontane rivers. Both these species have a well-defined feeding territory. The Pike and Mudminnow do not pursue food, but lie quietly in wait in the cover of plant growth, suddenly darting forward from the ambush. The Perch, however, hunts in organized shoals.

There is also food on the water surface or just above it: aquatic and terrestrial insects which have fallen on to the surface or are flying near it all present an opportunity for surface species such as alburns or the Ziege.

Many species use several feeding strategies and can be considered opportunistic feeders. The Brown Trout, for example, finds food both on the bottom, where it gathers insects, and in the water column, where it hunts fish. It is nevertheless also able to swim up to the surface to seize a drowning mayfly or jump out of the water for a careless fly.

Various types of mouth position have evolved in fish (Fig. 13) to suit the way in which food is obtained. Fishes that hunt or feed in the water column, for example the Trout or Chub, have a terminal mouth. Fishes which feed predominantly at the bottom have a ventral or inferior mouth, for example the East European Bream or Nase. Surface-feeding fishes have a dorsal or superior mouth, including the Rudd, Ziege or the alburns.

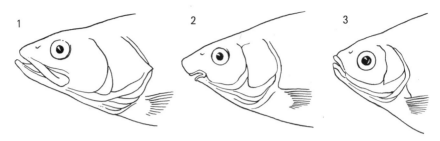

Fig. 13. Fish mouth positions: 1—terminal, 2—inferior, 3—superior

Fish species that live on the bottom tend to have either a cylindrical body, like the Gudgeon, or a snake-like shape like the Loach or Eel. A very different body form is found in flatfish, however, which have a laterally flattened body that lies on one side.

Fishes that live in the water column but which feed on the bottom generally have a flat belly and an arched back, as can be seen in carps and sturgeons. The mouth is ventral and varies in shape from trunk-like and protrusible, as in the Sterlet, Carp or Common Bream, through the slit-like mouth of the Nase to the benthic mouth of other sturgeons. A more or less straight back and markedly arched belly can be found among species that feed near the surface, such as the Alburn and Ziege, which have a dorsal mouth.

Different species also show different feeding regimes. Whereas the Gudgeon feeds intensively throughout the whole year, its close relative the Carp is most active in the summer. The Burbot is by contrast most active as a hunter in winter, whilst the Tench sleeps both in winter and in summer, which leaves it the spring and autumn to fatten itself up. Salmon do not hunt during their migration to the spawning site, whilst the adult Lampern does not eat at all. Each species thus has its own different adaptations, not all of which can be mentioned here. We shall, therefore, become acquainted with them in greater detail in the survey of species.

REPRODUCTION AND PARENTAL CARE

After feeding, reproduction is the second most important manifestation of fish behaviour. Whereas food ensures the survival of the individual, reproduction ensures the survival of the species.

The layman is usually struck by the enormous production of eggs in some species. The freshwater Burbot, for example, produces up to

3 million eggs, the Common Mullet as many as 7 million eggs. The eggs float freely, suspended in the water (pelagic), without any care or protection on the part of the parent fish. The vast majority of eggs and larval fish perish but the apparent overproduction ensures that at least a small proportion survives.

Fish species which show parental care tend to produce far fewer eggs. The small Bitterling can afford to lay only 40—100 eggs, because it lays them inside the security of mussel shells. The male Three-spined Stickleback, on the other hand, builds a nest of aquatic plants for the eggs, reminiscent of a bird's nest. The female lays into it 60—600 eggs, which are carefully guarded by the male, which also takes care of the alevins after they hatch. In many fish species, it is the male that takes over the care of eggs and young. In terms of equal rights greatest progress has been made by pipefishes. The female Broadnose Pipefish lays 50—300 eggs into the belly pouch of the male and he carries them until they hatch. Viviparous fishes provide greater security for their eggs, fertilisation and development of the young fish occurring inside the body of the female. In the case of the Mosquito Fish, the male transfers sperm by means of metamorphosed rays of his anal fin (gonopodia). The female eventually gives birth to up to 50 live and fully formed young.

Some species migrate upstream into higher reaches to spawn, ensuring ideal conditions for the development of eggs and alevins. The Brown Trout, for example, leaves its native section of brook just prior to spawning and swims upstream to places where the water is clear, rich in oxygen and where there are fewer predators. With Brown Trout, this migration is relatively short, but there are species which migrate several hundred kilometres to spawn, often having to overcome numerous obstacles in the process. The Salmon, a relative of the Brown Trout, migrates from the sea as far the upper reaches of rivers (anadromous migration). In fact it returns to its native river; it locates this using the taste and smell of the water, even if this is diluted to a ratio of 1:1 million.

Some species of mullet and the Eel migrate from fresh water to the sea to spawn (catadromous migration). The Eel has to swim through the sea for several thousand kilometres to its spawning grounds in the Sargasso Sea.

By comparison, gudgeon and bullheads are rather sedentary. They do not leave their favoured habitat at any time in their lives and indeed most fishes spawn close to home. In most cases they lay their eggs on to aquatic plants, branches, roots, stones, or the gravel and sand on the bottom. The eggs are viscous and generally adhere to the substrate or the bottom. Their development time depends upon the fish species and water temperature. Eggs of the Brown Trout take about 120—150 days at a temperature of 1—6 °C, whereas carp eggs take only a few days at a temperature of 18—20 °C. As a general rule eggs develop faster the higher the temperature.

The larvae rest after hatching until they have digested the food reserves in their yolk-sac. In species which stick their eggs on to plants and similar objects, the larvae often have a viscous organ used for clinging to substrates. The larvae of fishes which spawn on the bottom tend to conceal themselves in hollows in the bottom or amongst the roots of aquatic plants. After digesting the yolk-sac, the alevins swim off and begin to feed actively.

The importance of water temperature for the life of fishes has already been referred to several times. In most species an increase in temperature is the signal for spawning, for example for the Eel the temperature must rise above 20 °C. Thermophilic species begin to spawn with an increase in temperature, cool-loving species on the other hand with a drop in temperature. The Brown Trout and Eelpout, for example, spawn at temperatures ranging from 1 to 6 °C. Most species, however, do not have such extreme requirements for water temperature. These species spawn in the spring season.

Species which spawn in pairs are often outstandingly colourful, especially the males (for example the East Europan Bream, Three-spined Stickleback, Sunfish, etc.). The spawning of these species is generally preceded by a complex and lengthy ritual of posturing and movements. Fishes which spawn collectively develop a spawning rash, which is white-coloured, epidermal papillae, the task of which is to roughen the body surface and thus increase the stimulative effect of mutual contact, thereby assisting the spawning process.

Most fish need precise and stable environmental conditions before they can reproduce. Not surprisingly, many spawning sites have disappeared as a result of human activity, e.g. the canalization of courses and the construction of dams. The pollution of waters has moreover caused such a degree of deterioration in the conditions for many species that they are now unable to reproduce and are threatened with extinction. In the case of economically significant species, Man supplements the declining natural population by encouraging artificial spawning conditions, by farming alevins and then transferring them to open waters. For economically unimportant species, however, the altered conditions mean the threat of extinction.

MATURITY

The rate of growth in fish depends on the quantity of food consumed, which in turn is related to the temperature. As a general rule, in freshwater systems there is more food in warmer waters, species inhabiting these growing faster and attaining a larger size. There are, however, exceptions to this rule. In the previous section on food it was mentioned that the Burbot takes most food at low temperatures and the Tench does not grow during the warmer summer months simply because it is having its 'summer sleep'. There is considerable variation in temperature throughout the geographical area of Europe as well as throughout the year. Not surprisingly, the coolest water is found in mountain courses, which are also relatively poor in terms of food. Brown Trout from these localities therefore grow to a length of only 15—17 cm, whereas trout from lower and therefore warmer elevations grow to lengths of over 20 cm. It emerges from this that fish of the same species grow faster in warmer waters and grow to a greater size, the reason for this being the better food supplies as well as the extended feeding period throughout the year. The growth of fish depends not only on the quantity of food, but also on the abundance of competing mouths. For example, the more Crucian Carp in a pool, the less food available per fish and the slower their growth. The growth of any particular species is, however, more or less defined within hereditary limits. For this reason Panizza's Goby only grows to a length of 3—5 cm, seldom reaching 6 cm. Mosquito Fish males grow to 4.5—7 cm and the Moderlieschen to 5—6 cm. These are the smallest European fish species and will not grow any larger even under ideal conditions or no matter what age they reach.

In the past, the largest European species was the Beluga. In fresh waters specimens 5—8 m long and weighing 1,200—1,500 kg used to be caught. Excessive fishing and other detrimental human activities, however, have resulted in a reduction in the size of catches to 2—3 m with a weight of 65—150 kg per fish. Because of this, the Catfish now ranks among present-day freshwater giants. Regrettably, many fishes do not have time to grow to record sizes, being caught by fishermen long before then.

A fish's age is closely linked with its size. As a general rule the smaller the fish species, the lower the age it lives to. The small species mentioned above live for only 1—3 years. In contrast with this, the greatest age reached by a Beluga was 78 years and in a Catfish over 80 years. Too many dangers lie in wait for fishes in natural conditions, so that the majority of them do not die of old age. The maxi-

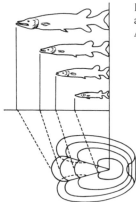

Fig. 14. Determination of the age of
a fish according to the scales:
A pair of concentric circles corresponds to one year of life

mum age of a fish is determined after it has been caught, which often means that its life is brought to an end prematurely.

In the Czech Republic two age records have been set under artificial conditions. The first of these was a Brown Trout, which was kept in a well and lived to be 49 years old. The second record-holder is an Eel, which lived to be 68 years old in the pool of a Prague insurance company. The fact that the Eel was prevented from migrating to the sea to spawn prolonged its life for several decades. In spite of the respectable age attained, however, neither of the above-mentioned fish achieved a great size. The trout measured 48 cm and weighed 900 g, the Eel was 66.5 cm long and weighed only 580 g.

What fisherman would not want to determine the age of a catch if he has landed a champion fish? If the fish has scales, its age can fortunately be determined without killing it (fig. 14). The scales in fact grow in concentric circles in a similar manner to the growth rings in trees. In a period of abundant food, these circles are far apart, whilst in a time of shortage, that is mostly in winter, the circles are denser and closer together. In this way pairs of light and dark concentric circles alternate on the scales, corresponding to the summer and winter seasons which have been undergone, each pair corresponding to one year of life.

Since the growth rate of fishes is more or less steady, it is possible to calculate the previous growth rate of a fish from its length and age. This retrospective calculation of the growth rate is useful for fish farmers when assessing conditions either in the wild or within the fish farm. Knowledge of growth rates for individual courses or reservoirs enables one to select the most suitable species for farming or to take measures to improve environmental conditions.

COLOUR PLATES

Hagfish
Myxine glutinosa
Myxinidae

The Hagfish is distributed along the European shores of the Atlantic Ocean from Murmansk as far as the western coast of the Mediterranean Sea, as well as along the North American Atlantic coast.

It occurs predominantly in the littoral belt at depths of 20-60 m, where it leads a typical parasitic mode of life. It prefers places where there are sea currents, which bring food scents to it. During the day it digs itself into the sand, with only the head protruding, swimming out for food only during the night. During the day it consumes various invertebrate animals, although its main diet consists of fish. These comprise not only those swimming about freely, but also those which are sick, dead or caught up in nets. It bites into them and eats the body contents. It first breaks the skin with its rasping tongue and then tears out the muscles. In order to achieve the necessary degree of traction, it twists its body into a knot, resting the loop against the surface of the fish. The largish, oval aperture on the side of the anterior part of the body is the gill outlet. Its location further from the head than in most other fish is an adaptation to its parasitic mode of life. Whilst feeding, the head is often partly hidden inside the body of its prey. It often attacks fish collectively. A case is known in which 213 Hagfish were found in one caught cod.

The Hagfish matures at a size of 25-28 cm. It leaves the coast to spawn, descending to greater depths, where it deposits 20-30 large eggs on the bottom. There is no particular breeding season, spawning occurring at any time of year. From the economic point of view it is a harmful species which damages and kills fish caught in fishing equipment.

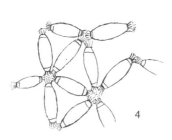

4

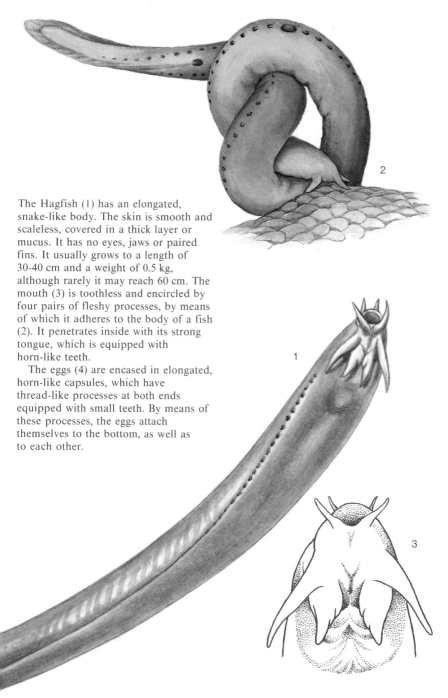

The Hagfish (1) has an elongated, snake-like body. The skin is smooth and scaleless, covered in a thick layer or mucus. It has no eyes, jaws or paired fins. It usually grows to a length of 30-40 cm and a weight of 0.5 kg, although rarely it may reach 60 cm. The mouth (3) is toothless and encircled by four pairs of fleshy processes, by means of which it adheres to the body of a fish (2). It penetrates inside with its strong tongue, which is equipped with horn-like teeth.

The eggs (4) are encased in elongated, horn-like capsules, which have thread-like processes at both ends equipped with small teeth. By means of these processes, the eggs attach themselves to the bottom, as well as to each other.

29

Brook Lamprey
Lampetra planeri

The Brook Lamprey inhabits brooks and small rivers which flow into the North and Baltic Seas. As recently as 1969 it was also discovered in the area which feeds the Black Sea in the Danube river basin. It spends most of its life buried in sandy layers in shallows or in bays, leaving its hiding place only rarely and then only at night. It is only possible to catch sight of it on the bottom in open water from April to June, during the spawning period. At that time Brook Lampreys gather in large numbers at the spawning sites, where the female builds pits — nests for the eggs — in the shallow water of the sands. The female clings to a stone at the edge of the future nest by means of the oral discs, and with undulating movements whirls the sand, which is carried away by the current. She rolls larger stones away with the head. The males only arrive at the spawning site when the nest is ready. Shortly after spawning, the parental Brook Lamprey perish from exhaustion. Adult Brook Lampreys do not feed and their digestive system is atrophied. They grow to 12-16 cm in length. The larvae are somewhat larger than the adults, measuring up to 18 cm before metamorphosis. In view of its small size and infrequent occurrence, the Brook Lamprey is of no economic importance.

The Danube Lamprey (*Eudontomyzon danfordi*) inhabits the upper reaches of the Danube and its tributaries, as well as rivers south-west of the Danube. It lives 4-5 years in the larval stage in the sandy and muddy layers of the bottom, where it feeds on detritus and small organisms. Adult specimens cling to both live and dead fish with their mouths and feed on their blood and musculature. Danube Lampreys spawn collectively in the second year of their adult life, and perish afterwards. This species is of no economic significance either.

Spawning in the Danube Lamprey is similar to that in the Brook Lamprey. The partners first swim round each other above the nest and the female then clings with her mouth to the edge of the nest.

2

The male then wraps his body around the female in such a way that their sexual orifices will come closer to each other. While doing this, the male holds on to the back of the female's head with his oral disc (1). Spawning lasts longer than a week and usually there are up to 1,500 eggs. Males differ from females in having a smaller anal border and a tube-like elongated urogenital papilla.

The Danube Lamprey (2) differs from the Brook Lamprey in its larger size and divided lobes of the dorsal fin border. It grows to 15-26 cm, weighing 40-60 g. The oral disc of the adult Brook Lamprey (3) is not used for feeding and has only a small number of blunt teeth. The parasitic Danube Lamprey, on the other hand, has a functional mouth with a larger number of sharp teeth (4) in its oral disc.

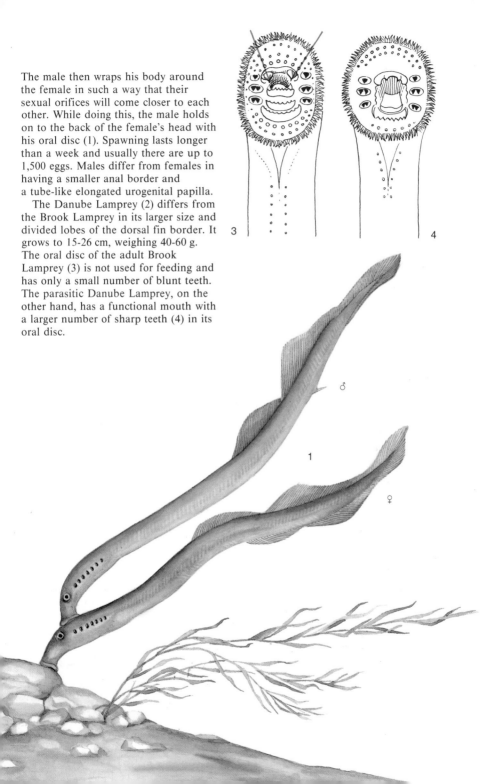

3

4

♂

1

♀

The Lampern
Lampetra fluviatilis

Petromyzonidae

The Lampern is distributed along the Baltic Sea coast, the shores of southern Norway and the British Isles, along the whole of the Atlantic coast, as far east as Italy in the Mediterranean Sea, as well as in the rivers of this region. Isolated, permanently freshwater populations live in the Lagoda and Onega lakes.

On the sea coast, Lampern live for 1-2 years. Sexually mature Lampern migrate collectively to rivers from August to November in order to spawn. A small proportion of the population do not migrate until early in the spring of the following year. During this migration they do not feed and their digestive organs degenerate. Their colouring changes to a metallic bronze, the originally sharp teeth becoming blunt during migration, and the anal fin of the female increases in size. Spawning begins in February in the upper reaches of rivers, being started by those Lampern which have passed the winter there. The female beats out a bowl-like depression in the sandy or gravelly bed by means of her enlarged anal fin. At the edge of the newly dug nest, she then clings to a stone with her head positioned against the stream. The male attaches himself with his mouth to the back of her neck and encircles her with his body in such a way that their cloacae are close to each other. The female lays 4,000-40,000 eggs into the nest. After spawning, both the males and females perish. Larvae hatch from the eggs and live buried in the sand of the river bed feeding on organic debris. The larval development lasts for 3-5 years. When reaching a length of 9-15 cm, metamorphosis of larva to adult occurs, and the metamorphosed individuals migrate into the sea. Lampern meat is tasty and fatty. They are caught during migration, mainly in the rivers which feed the Baltic.

4   2

The Lampern (1) has a snake-like body with a divided dorsal fin. During the period of spawning, the two parts of the fin in the female enlarge until they join together. The oral funnel is equipped with teeth (2) and there are 7 gill apertures on the surface of the skin. Lampern grow to a length of 30-40 cm, their weight reaching about 350 g and in exceptional cases up to 50 cm and 700 g. They feed on marine invertebrates and dead fish, also parasitise live fish, adhering to them by means of the oral sucker.

The sharp teeth break the skin, releasing
a secretion from the oral glands into the
wound which prevents coagulation of
the blood. It then sucks the blood, body
fluids and damaged musculature from
the wound.

A Lampern larva (3), formerly
described as a separate genus
Ammocoetes, is blind and has
a horseshoe-like, toothless mouth (4)
and gill apertures hidden
in a fold of skin.

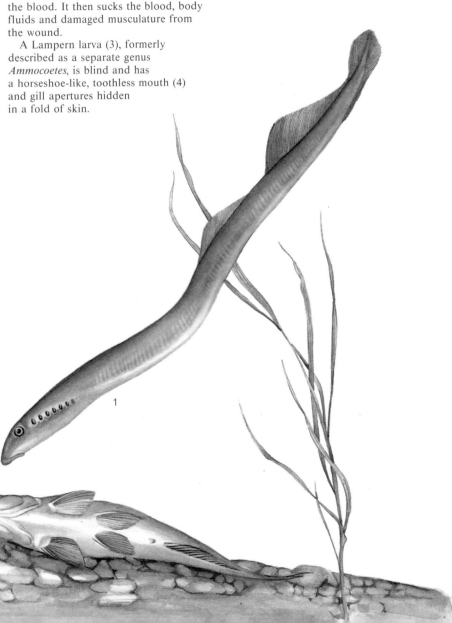

The Sea Lamprey
Petromyzon marinus

Petromyzonidae

The Sea Lamprey inhabits the Atlantic coast of Europe, from the White Sea in the north as far as Italy in the Mediterranean Sea, and in America the northern Atlantic coast from Nova Scotia to Florida.

It lives in the sea in the littoral zone at depths down to 500 m. In the spring sexually mature Sea Lamprey migrate to rivers, where they spawn from May to June in the current on a stony or gravelly bed. The female prepares a nest for the eggs before actual spawning, consisting of a depression up to 2 m long and 1 m wide in the bed. When forming the nest, the female is able to roll stones up to 1 kg in weight away from the chosen place. She lays 34,000-250,000 transparent eggs. During migration to the spawning site and during spawning itself, Sea Lamprey do not feed and perish from exhaustion after spawning. A proportion of Sea Lamprey, however, spawn on the sea coast. These individuals survive the spawning, and spawn several more times in the sea. The larvae hatch after 1-2 weeks, and their eyes are covered over with skin. At this stage they have toothless, horseshoe-like mouths. In rivers, they keep to the bed in muddy reaches, feeding on microplankton filtered from the water. After 2-5 years they reach a size of 15-20 cm, metamorphose into young Sea Lamprey and migrate to the sea, where they are parasitic on fish. After 3-4 years they reach sexual maturity and migrate back to the rivers to spawn.

In the past the Sea Lamprey used to be of great significance both for sea fishing and the management of flowing waters. Owing to the construction of waterworks, however, spawning migration has ceased in many rivers, so that the numbers of Sea Lamprey and thus also its economic importance have decreased. Another adverse factor reducing the Sea Lamprey population is river pollution.

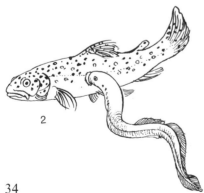

2

The Sea Lamprey (1) is the largest species of the Petromyzonidae family. It grows to a length of 50-80 cm and 3 kg. If feeds on the blood and flesh of fish (2), attaching to the body of a fish with its oral disc. It breaks the skin and muscles with its sharp teeth and tongue and then sucks out the blood and crushed musculature using its tongue like a piston.

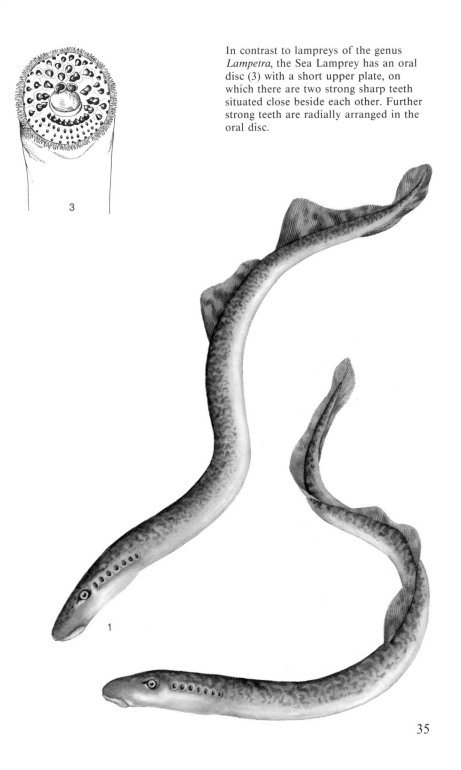

In contrast to lampreys of the genus *Lampetra*, the Sea Lamprey has an oral disc (3) with a short upper plate, on which there are two strong sharp teeth situated close beside each other. Further strong teeth are radially arranged in the oral disc.

3

1

Sterlet
Acipenser ruthenus

Acipenseridae

The Sterlet lives in rivers feeding the Caspian and Black Seas and the Sea of Azov, as well as in rivers which flow into the Ladoga and Onega lakes. In rivers feeding the Arctic Ocean it occurs from the Ob to the Kolyma. It occasionally occurs in river estuaries flowing into the White Sea, for example in the North Dvina.

It is the only member of the genus *Acipenser* that permanently lives in fresh waters. It inhabits deeper places in the main course of the river, also penetrating high into the tributaries. It survives the winter in a state of rest and without food in the depths of the lower section of the course. During the spring months it migrates to higher reaches for spawning. From March to June, the females lay 11,000-140,000 viscous eggs. For the first nine years of their lives the older the females, the more eggs they produce. Thereafter, however, the number of eggs drops steadily. The females leave the spawning site after spawning, the males staying there longer and spawning with other females. The hatched fry drift downstream to the lower reaches, where they stay and feed actively on small invertebrates. Adult fish eat the benthic fauna. At night they swim out of deeper places towards the bank, where they catch insects which have fallen on to the surface. As the mouth is on the ventral part of the head, it has to turn belly upwards when seizing quarry.

The Sterlet is a valuable fish for anglers. It crossbreeds with related larger species, the cross-breeds staying permanently in fresh water, thus being eminently suitable for introducing into lakes, dams and some ponds.

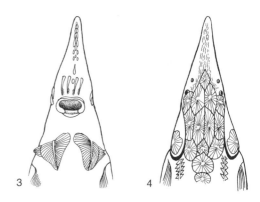

3   4

36

The Sterlet (1) is the most abundant and at the same time the smallest *Acipenser* species, reaching a length of 50-60 cm and 2-3 kg in weight, rarely up to 125 cm and 19 kg. Like other sturgeon species, its head is elongated into a snout of greatly varying length. The skin is smooth and there are altogether five rows of bony plates on the back, sides and belly. The bony plates of the dorsal row (2) have a curved tip pointing towards the tail. The lower ones are anchored in the skin with their flat side. The caudal fin is asymmetrical, the upper lobe being longer. On the head of the members of this genus, there are important features for identifying them. The Sterlet has a ventral, toothless mouth, with the lower lip divided into two parts. Four small fleshy barbels on the lower part of the snout are bristly on the inner side (3). Individual species also differ in the arrangement of bony plates on the upper part of the head. Plate 4 shows the arrangement of bony plates in the Sterlet.

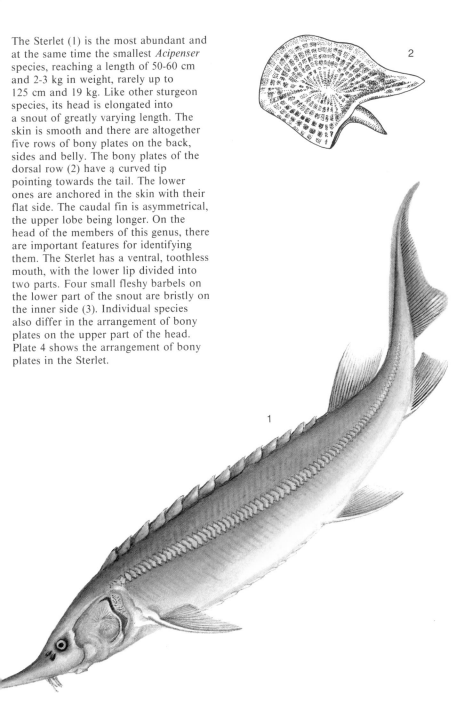

Russian Sturgeon
Acipenser güldenstädti

Acipenseridae

The Russian Sturgeon occurs in the Black, Azov and Caspian Seas and in large rivers of the north-western part of the area which feeds these seas.

They mature relatively late; males between the 8-15th years, females between the 13-20th years, but they live up to 46 years. Part of the adult population migrates in shoals from the sea against the stream of rivers to higher reaches as early as in the autumn, staying there over the winter. The remaining adult individuals do not set out for the spawning site until the spring and spawn immediately after arriving. During migration, they cover up to 30 km a day. Apart from the migratory Russian Sturgeon, populations permanently inhabiting fresh water also exist. The Russian Sturgeon originally used to spawn in the flood zone of gravelly banks in the upper reaches of large rivers, but owing to the construction of valley reservoirs the routes to many traditional spawning sites have been cut off. It therefore uses the gravelly bottom of the main river bed in the lower reaches of courses as a substitute. Spawning begins in May and thanks to the fish of the spring migration is prolonged until as late as August. The fry are at first light-sensitive and hide in crevices in the river bed. After several days, they leave their hiding places, and the greater proportion of them drift downstream into the lower reaches of the river. In their 3rd or 4th year the young fish leave the fresh water of rivers and swim out to the sea.

Adult individuals eat very little during their journey to the spawning sites. After spawning they try to make up for their losses with an increased food intake as they return to the sea. They dig out invertebrates from the bed with their snout and gather them with the snout-like, protrusible mouth. The largest ones hunt small benthic fishes.

Because of its good quality meat with a high fat content and its eggs, from which caviare is prepared, the Russian Sturgeon is an economically important fish species.

The Russian Sturgeon (1), together with the Ship Sturgeon, ranks among the smaller European sturgeons. The average length of males is 155 cm, of females 175 cm, reaching a weight of 12-24 kg. Only occasionally are individuals caught which are 220-235 cm long and weighing up to 80 kg.

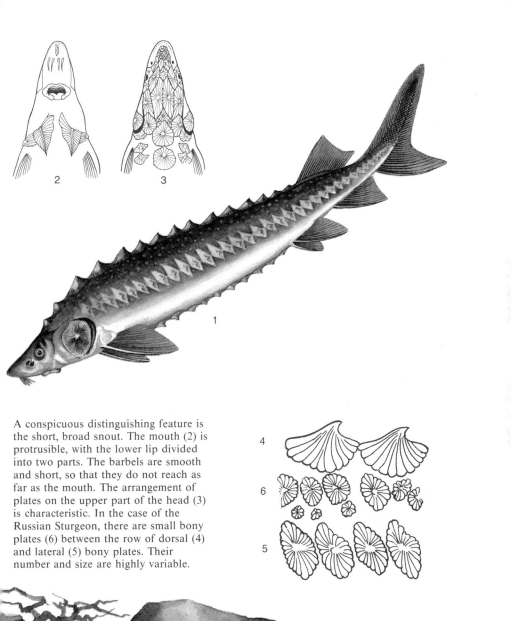

A conspicuous distinguishing feature is the short, broad snout. The mouth (2) is protrusible, with the lower lip divided into two parts. The barbels are smooth and short, so that they do not reach as far as the mouth. The arrangement of plates on the upper part of the head (3) is characteristic. In the case of the Russian Sturgeon, there are small bony plates (6) between the row of dorsal (4) and lateral (5) bony plates. Their number and size are highly variable.

Ship Sturgeon
Acipenser nudiventris
Acipenseridae

The Ship Sturgeon is distributed in the Caspian, Aral and Black Seas and the rivers which feed them. Along the sea coast it keeps to depths of up to 50 m. It stays in the sea until reaching maturity, which in the case of males occurs in the 6-9th year, and in the case of females in the 12-14th year. It can live for more than 30 years.

It migrates to the central and lower reaches of rivers to spawn. In both the Caspian and the Black Sea, spawning migration begins as early as autumn, being at its peak in October. The fish from the autumn migration overwinter in the rivers, and early in spring, when the water temperature rises above 10 °C, spawning begins. In April and May, the fish from the spring migration arrive at the spawning sites, also taking part in spawning. The Aral Sea is inhabited predominantly by the autumn migrating race. The Ship Sturgeon does not spawn regularly each year, but only once every two to three years. This fact is compensated for by its high fecundity. A single female lays 280,000-1,290,000 eggs 3 mm in size. At a temperature of 10-15 °C, the fry usually hatch after 7 days. A smaller proportion of young drift out to sea during the summer, the majority, however, remaining in the lower reaches of rivers for more than a year.

The Ship Sturgeon's diet consists mainly of molluscs, stonefly larvae and other small benthic fauna, including fishes. It gulps food from the bottom together with a great deal of mud, sand and other particles. It is most numerous in the Caspian Sea, therefore forming there a significant proportion of catches of economically exploited fish species. Caviar is prepared from the roe of the Ship Sturgeon.

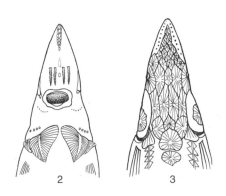

2   3

The Ship Sturgeon (1) grows to a length of 150-200 cm and a weight of 17-20 kg at the age of 20 years. In isolated cases specimens have been caught weighing over 40 kg. A record fish weighing 127 kg was caught in 1925.

The Ship Sturgeon has a small mouth. The lower lip is not divided and the barbels are fringed (2). The first bony plate on the back (3) towers above the others in size, there being 11-16 of these on the back, 52-74 on the sides and 11-17 on the belly. The head of the young fish is conspicuously large (4), standing out particularly when viewed from above (5).

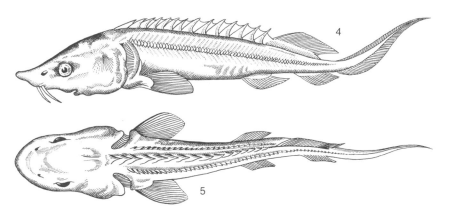

Starry Sturgeon
Acipenser stellatus   Acipenseridae

The habitat of the Starry Sturgeon is the Black and Caspian Seas and the rivers feeding them. Recently it has been introduced into the Sea of Aral, where hitherto the only representative of the Acipenseridae family had been the Ship Sturgeon. It is a migratory fish, forming two races — the autumn and the spring one. It matures sexually at the age of 8-15 years, not leaving the sea until that time. It migrates to rivers to spawn. The autumn race swims into rivers in October and November, overwintering there. The spring race overwinters in the sea, withdrawing from the sea coast to depths of 80-100 m. It migrates to rivers from March to June. During the spawning migration the fish do not take any food, swimming 17-32 km daily. The spawning sites are distributed from river estuaries as far as their middle reaches, for example in the Volga as far as 350 km from its estuary. Spawning itself takes place from April to August. The female lays 20,000—633,000 viscous eggs on the bed. At a temperature of 20 °C the fry hatch from them after 5 days. The adult fish leave the spawning site after spawning, returning to the sea. Aided by the current, they swim faster than when migrating upwards to the spawning site, covering up to 70 km a day. The fry drift downstream gradually. Their progress, however, is much slower, and it takes 2-3 months until they reach the sea. The diet of a young Starry Sturgeon consists of bottom-dwelling invertebrates, mainly crustaceans and the larvae of Chironomids. In the adult Sturgeon, the diet is supplemented by fishes. It commonly grows to a length of 100-150 cm and in rare cases up to 220 cm with a weight of up to 70 kg.

The Starry Sturgeon is an economically important species, its meat being very tasty and black caviar being prepared from the roe.

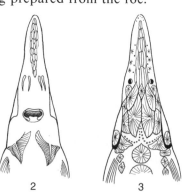

2   3

The sides of the Starry Sturgeon (1) are covered with small star-shaped platelets among rows of bony scutes. Its sword-like bent snout is the longest of all European sturgeons, its length being greater than half the head length. On the ventral part of the head (2) four smooth, fleshy barbels grow in front of the mouth, and the lower lip is divided by a groove into two parts. The head scutes (3) are divided from the ones on the body by small star-shaped platelets. The number of dorsal scutes range from 9 to 16, lateral scutes from 26 to 43, and ones on the belly from 9 to 14. Like all other sturgeon species, the Starry Sturgeon has an asymmetrical (heterocercous) caudal fin (4), the upper lobe being elongated and the tail peduncle penetrating into it.

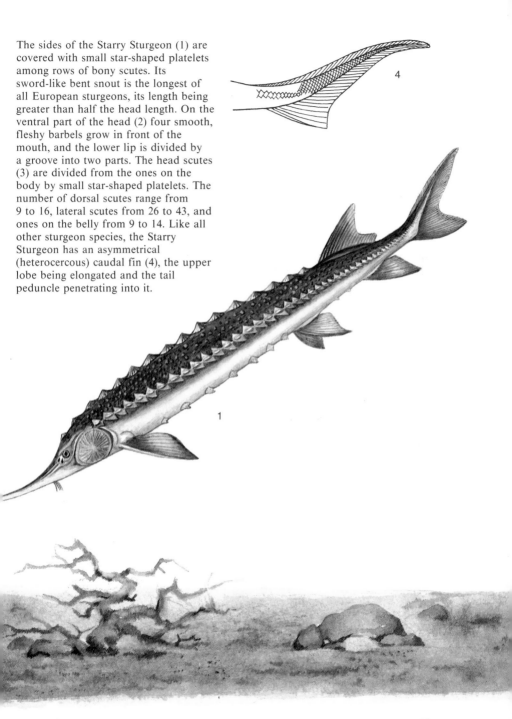

Common Sturgeon
Acipenser sturio
Acipenseridae

In the past, the Common Sturgeon used to live along the whole coast of Europe as far as the North Sea. Nowadays it has almost completely been exterminated along the western coast as far as Poland, where it is a protected species. The largest, not particularly abundant, population lives in the Black Sea region. It can also be encountered on the eastern coast of North America.

It is a migratory fish which penetrates fresh waters only during the spawning period. An exception is the permanent population living in Lake Ladoga. For most of the year, Common Sturgeon lead a solitary existence, joining together to form shoals only in the spring in order to spawn, and in autumn for overwintering. It enters rivers in April and May, not spawning until June and July. It spawns in the central reaches of rivers in the current over a stony bed at a depth of 2-10 m. The female lays up to 2,400,000 viscous eggs, the development of which takes 3-5 days. The fry and young remain in fresh water until autumn at the latest, then swimming out to sea. The males mature at an age of 7-9 years, the females somewhat later, at 8-14 years. At first they feed on small invertebrates, mostly crustaceans, polychaete worms and molluscs. Adult individuals hunt fishes that live on or near the bottom.

Nowadays the numbers of Common Sturgeon are so low that its economic significance is minimal. The blame for this lies not only in overfishing, but also in the elimination and pollution of the spawning sites.

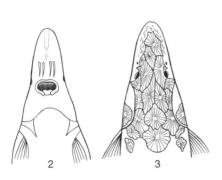

The Common Sturgeon (1) is the second largest species of the Acipenseridae family after the Beluga, growing to a length of almost 300 cm and reaching a weight of up to 200 kg. In 1909 a record fish was caught in the North Sea, measuring 345 cm and weighing 320 kg. It lives to a great age, ages of up to 40 years commonly being mentioned.

The lower lip is broken by a groove. The barbels are smooth, being located quite far from the end of the snout and closer to the mouth (2). A view from above (3) shows the position of the head scutes.

2　　　　3

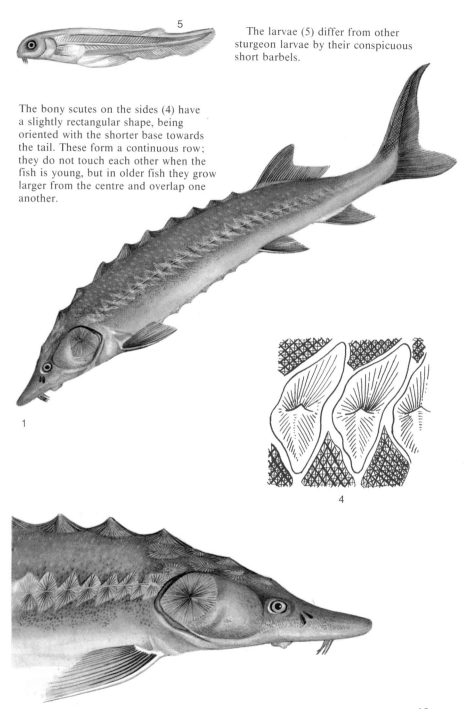

The larvae (5) differ from other sturgeon larvae by their conspicuous short barbels.

The bony scutes on the sides (4) have a slightly rectangular shape, being oriented with the shorter base towards the tail. These form a continuous row; they do not touch each other when the fish is young, but in older fish they grow larger from the centre and overlap one another.

45

Beluga
Huso huso
Acipenseridae

To spawn, the Beluga swims from the Caspian and Black Seas and the Sea of Azov to lowland and submontane reaches of large European rivers, that is the Volga, the Don, the Danube and others. In the Mediterranean Sea it lives along the Italian coast in the vicinity of the Po estuary. It spends most of its life in the sea in the littoral belt near river estuaries. For the winter it withdraws to deeper places, in the Black Sea as deep as 180 m.

According to the season of spawning migration, two races can be distinguished in the Beluga. The autumn race spawns further upstream, in the Don for example 500-600 km from the estuary, and therefore it swims into the rivers as early as September and October. By winter it has swum to the central reaches and after overwintering in pits on the bottom of the river it continues its journey to the spawning site. The spring race spawns in the lowland reaches of the middle sections of courses. It sets out from the sea in March and April, spawning in May over the gravelly and stony bed of the main stream. The viscous eggs attach themselves to the bottom, their numbers ranging from 300,000 to 7,000,000. At a temperature of 13 °C the fry hatch after approximately a week, and slowly drift downstream to the sea. They are able to feed independently after ten days, at first hunting smaller invertebrates, more grown-up individuals also hunting fish. Fish then become the exclusive diet of larger specimens. A size of 1 m is reached by Belugas at the age of 4 years, and 2 m at the age of 16 years. Males mature in their 12-14th year, females in their 10-20th year. The Beluga can live for up to 100 years. It is of great economic importance on account of its roe, of which the world-famous black caviar is made.

The Beluga (1) is the largest living sturgeon. In the past, specimens 5-8 m long weighing 1,200-1,500 kg used to be caught. The size of contemporary catches has dropped to 2-3 m and 65-150 kg in weight. A conspicuous feature of the Beluga is the large, broad, crescent-shaped mouth (2). The short fleshy barbels are flat and extend on to

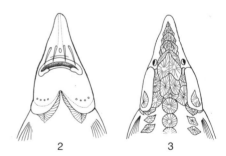

2   3

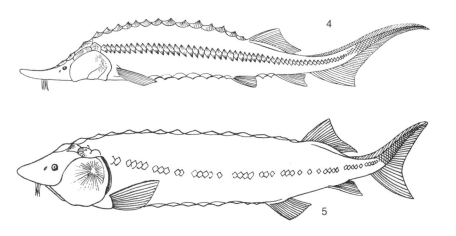

the upper lip. Skin membranes bordering the gills are fused together in the middle of the throat, forming a continuous transverse border on the ventral part of the head. The scutes on the upper part of the head (3) are characteristically arranged.

In the case of young individuals (4) the snout is relatively long, the bony plates are not worn down and are in complete rows. Old specimens (5) have a short, broad snout and the bony plates are worn down, often having even fallen out. The overall body morphology and proportion of the fin size in relation to the body change with age, this being particularly striking in the case of the caudal fin.

Allis Shad
Alosa alosa
Clupeidae

The Allis Shad lives along the coast of western Europe from southern Norway as far south as Spain, in the Mediterranean Sea extending eastwards along the coast as far as western Italy and Sicily.

It spends most of its life in salt water, but adult fishes migrate to fresh waters to spawn. They spawn from May to June in estuaries and lower reaches of rivers. Only rarely do they penetrate far upstream, as was once the case in the Rhine, where they used to migrate up to 800 km. The spawning sites are found in swift reaches over sandy or stony beds. After being spawned, the transparent eggs swell up greatly, and drift downstream to lower reaches. The fecundity of the female ranges from 250,000 to 350,000 eggs. The larvae hatch after 6-8 days. Whereas fish which have spawned return to the sea, the fry remain in fresh or brackish water until autumn. They then also swim out to sea, and mature between the 3rd and 4th years of their lives. In the sea the Allis Shad feeds predominantly on zooplankton, and in the brackish water of river estuaries on small crustaceans. Large specimens supplement their diet with small fishes.

Because of its tasty meat and great numbers, the Allis Shad was once of great economic importance. On account of river pollution, however, their numbers have reduced to such an extent that now they are fished for in only a few rivers and estuaries.

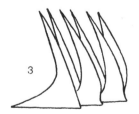

The Allis Shad (1) has a high, laterally-flattened body. The lateral line is lacking on the body, but its head branch on the lower jaw is well-developed. The eye is covered with fat pads both in front and behind, the fat pads being covered over with a transparent membrane.

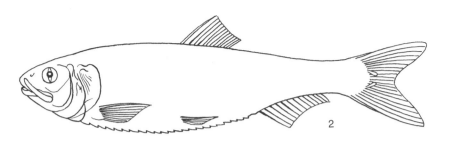

A characteristic distinguishing feature of the species is the large black spot behind the operculum. Other black spots on the body may differ in individual fish, both in number and in the intensity of colouring.

The Allis Shad commonly grows to a length of 30-50 cm, on rare occasions specimens about 70 cm in length and weighing up to 3.5 kg occur.

The distinguishing feature of the genus *Alosa* is the 'roof-tile' arrangement of the scales, which form a serrated keel on the edge of the belly (2). The scales of the belly keel are double-winged (3).

Finta Shad, Twaite Shad
Alosa fallax

Clupeidae

The Finta Shad is distributed along the Atlantic coast of Europe from southern Norway as far as the Pyrenean peninsula, in the Baltic, Mediterranean and Black Seas and in the rivers of this region. In contrast with the Allis Shad, it occurs only in the lower reaches of rivers up to about 100 km from the estuaries. In some large lakes, such as for example the Scutari, Killarney, Como, Lugano, Maggiore, Iseo and Garda lakes, live permanent freshwater populations.

In the sea it generally forms migratory populations which swim into fresh waters for spawning. Migration to the spawning site takes about a month, during which the fish do not take any food. They spawn in May and June over a sandy or gravelly bed. The fecundity of females ranges from 75,000 up to 200,000 eggs. As the eggs have a smooth surface, they are carried off by the current, and only those which fall into crevices in the bed remain at the spawning site. They take 2-8 days to develop at a temperature of 15-25 °C. The fry swim away to sea either in autumn or remain until the spring of the following year. In the sea the young fish grow relatively quickly, already measuring 8-14 cm at the age of one year. They keep to the littoral belt at depths ranging from shallows down to 100 m. They live mainly on crustaceans, large individuals also hunting small fishes.

The economic importance of the Finta Shad has declined as a consequence of a reduction in its numbers. It has relatively dry meat with a low fat content, and grows to a length of 25-40 cm, up to 500 cm and a weight of 1.5-2 kg if it reaches its maximum age limit of 20-25 years.

The Finta Shad (1) is a high-bodied fish similar to the Allis Shad, with 6-10 distinct black spots on its sides. The lateral line is absent on the body, only its head branches being developed. On each side, two large scales extend from the peduncle of the tail to the triangular-shaped sections of the caudal fin, being a characteristic feature of all species of the genus *Alosa*, as are also the small fat pads around the eyes.

Members of the genus *Alosa* are highly variable and often closely resemble one another. An important distinguishing feature is the number and shape of the gill-rakers on the gill arches. The Finta Shad has a smaller number of strong gill-rakers (2), which are usually of the same length as the gill lamellae. The Allis Shad has a greater number of thin, long gill-rakers (3) which are longer than the gill lamellae.

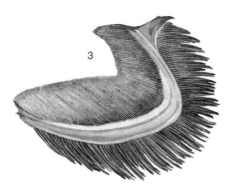

51

Caspian Shad
Alosa caspia

Clupeidae

The Caspian Shad forms several subspecies which are distributed in the Black and Caspian Seas and the Sea of Azov. It is generally a migratory species, most individuals swimming into the estuaries and lower reaches of rivers to spawn. Sporadically some specimens migrate even further upstream, for example the subspecies *Alosa caspia nordmanni* in the Danube as far as the Iron Gate. Exceptionally, some populations can spawn in the sea. Spawning takes place from the end of April until June at depths of 2-3 m. The fecundity of females ranges from 12,000 to 400,000 eggs. The eggs are semi-pelagic, their size somewhat increasing in water. The fry hatch after 2-3 days depending on the temperature, being carried slowly downstream by the current as far as the sea, where the young fish mature in the 2-3rd year of life. The Caspian Shad lives for 5-6 years, spawning 2-3 times in a lifetime. It is the smallest European species of the genus *Alosa*, growing to a length of only 20 cm, at most 32 cm, at a weight of 100-120 g. Its diet consists of zooplankton, to a lesser extent phytoplankton, parts of aquatic plants and small fishes. The Caspian Shad is fished for mainly in the Caspian Sea, where it forms over 50 per cent of herring catches.

One of the subspecies into which *Alosa caspia* is divided is *Alosa caspia nordmanni*. This is a semi-migratory fish which lives in the western part of the Black Sea, the eastern margin of its distribution being formed by the Crimea and western Turkey. It migrates up the Danube, Dniestr and Dnieper rivers to spawn. The smallest subspecies is *Alosa caspia tanaica*, which overwinters in the Black Sea, swimming into the Sea of Azov in spring and from there into the estuaries and lower reaches of the Don and Kuban rivers to spawn.

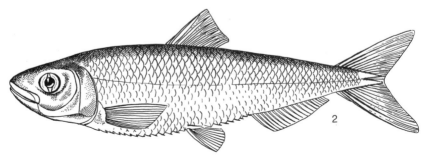

2

52

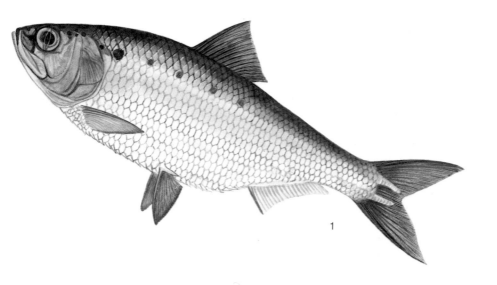

1

The Caspian Shad (1) has a short tail peduncle, thus giving the impression of a short, high-bodied fish. As in other species of the genus, the large eyes are covered with fat pads and a transparent membrane, the upper jaw of the large mouth extending behind the eye. The teeth are less developed than in other species, being found only on the lower jaw when the fish is young, and disappearing as it matures. The slender, long gill-rakers on the thin gill arch are adapted for filtering zooplankton. On each side of the caudal fin it has 2 large scales. Dark spots on the sides of the body are an outstanding feature. *Alosa caspia nordmanni* (2) grows to a length of only 18 cm, rarely to 25 cm, and has no dark spots on the sides. *Alosa caspia tanaica* (3) has 8 small dark spots on the sides. It grows to a length of 15 cm and a weight of 25 g, in isolated cases to 20 cm and 60 g.

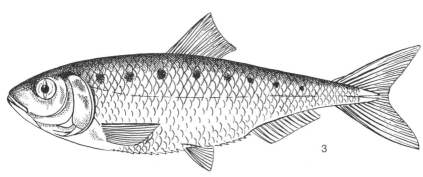

3

Black-backed Shad
Alosa kessleri

Clupeidae

The Black-backed Shad is the largest Caspian herring. Catches usually range in size from 20 to 40 cm with a weight of up to 1.8 kg. It is a migratory species, swimming in shoals from the end of March into the central reaches of rivers to spawn. In the first shoals of spring the fish are larger, being smaller at the end of the migration in June. They begin spawning during the spring thaw when the rivers break their banks and the temperature of the water rises to 15 °C. The Black-backed Shad is the most fecund herring in the Caspian Sea, the female laying 135,000-312,000 eggs in 2-3 batches at intervals of a few days. The majority of females perish after their first spawning. The eggs swell up after being fertilized, their size more than doubling. The fry swim out to sea after 1-2 months. The Black-backed Shad attains sexual maturity in the 5-6th year of its life. Initially it lives on larger planktonic fauna, adult specimens hunting smaller fishes. It is of considerable economic significance, being fished for mainly in the period of spawning migrations in the Volga delta. It is considered to have the best meat of all the Caspian herrings.

Alosa pontica migrates from the Black and Caspian Seas and the Sea of Azov for spawning to the lower reaches of large rivers such as the Danube, Dniestr, Bug, Don and Volga. It spawns in April and June over a sandy and gravelly bed. The fry drift downstream into the sea, where they mature.

Alosa brashnikovi is predominantly a sea species. From the Caspian Sea and the Sea of Azov it penetrates only rarely into the fresh water of the lowest reaches of rivers, occurring more frequently in river estuaries or in the brackish water of coastal lakes, such as the Razelm lake in the Danube delta.

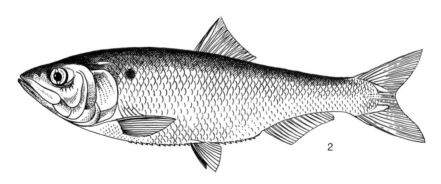

2

54

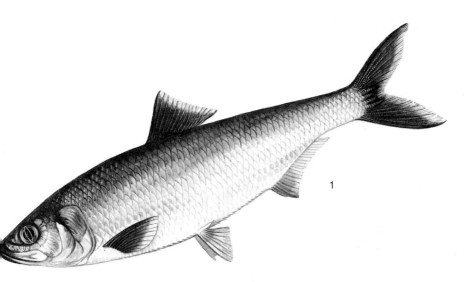

Compared with other herrings, the Black-backed Shad (1) has relatively vivid colouring, the back being dark violet and the top of the head, the dorsal and ventral fins being black. The black colouring of the tip of the snout creates a particularly contrasting effect. During sexual activity the back and sides turn a greenish-grey, golden yellow spots appearing on the back, sides and opercula, and the eyes being bordered by a golden yellow ring. A typical feature of the genus is the absence of the lateral line along the sides and prolonged scales at the base of the caudal fin. The well-developed teeth and short thick rakers on the gill arches are an adaptation to the predatory mode of life.

Alosa pontica (2) grows to a length of 15-20 cm, sometimes up to 41 cm. It can live for up to 7 years. It is a popular fish because of its tasty meat, which has a high fat content.

Alosa brashnikovi (3) is a predatory fish, commonly growing to lengths of 30-45 cm.

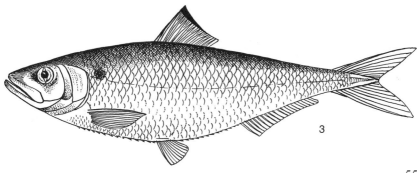

Sea Trout
Salmo trutta   Salmonidae

The Sea Trout is distributed along the north-western coast of Europe from Cheshskaya Bay in the Kara Sea to Duero river on the Pyrenean peninsula, in the Black and Caspian Seas and in the rivers of this region. It is a migratory species, leaving the coast only in the period of spawning, when it swims to rivers. If this sea species is prevented from leaving fresh waters and swimming back into the sea, it remains in fresh water and changes within 1-2 generations into a permanent fresh water form. This is mostly the Brown Trout (*Salmo trutta* m. *fario*), and in certain lakes the Lake Trout (*Salmo trutta* m. *lacustris*). Each year 1-2 per cent of young fish remain in fresh water of their own volition.

The spawning migration of the Sea Trout begins in spring, spawning itself taking place from September until January. The female prepares a depression or 'redd' into which she lays the eggs on the gravelly bed of smaller torrents. The nest can have a diameter of up to several metres and a depth of 1 m. Between 2,000 and 16,000 eggs are laid at a time, the spawned eggs then being covered over with gravel by the female. A smaller proportion of fish, predominantly males, perish after spawning. The majority, however, return to the sea. The fry hatch after 150 days and remain for varying lengths of time in fresh water, depending on the geographical latitude of the locality in which they occur. In the northern regions of its distribution, the Sea Trout remains in rivers for up to 7 years, less in the south, in some places only one year. It matures in its 3-8th year and can live for over 20 years. Migration has ceased in many rivers as a result of the pollution of rivers and the construction of high weirs and dams, the number of the species having decreased greatly as a consequence, and hence also its economic significance.

The Sea Trout (1) has a powerful, cylindrical body, growing to a length of 50-100 cm and a weight of 10-18 kg. Rarely, specimens up to 140 cm in length and weighing up to 50 kg occur. The spotting on the body is highly variable. It usually has only dark spots, less frequently also red spots with white bordering, which sometimes extend to below the lateral line. A striking feature

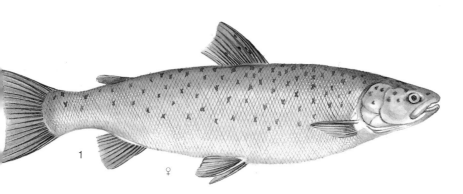

1

♀

of mature males is the powerful lower
jaw, which bends into a hook. The
female has a shorter, roundish head and
straight jaws, differing from the
brownish to brownish-orange males by
her bluish-grey colouring.

In salmonids the teeth grow on the
jaws (2), the palate (3) and on the vomer
(4). The number, location and shape of
the teeth on this bone are important
systematic features of the family.
The vomer is fully toothed only in
young fish.

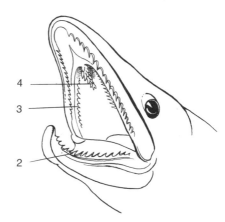

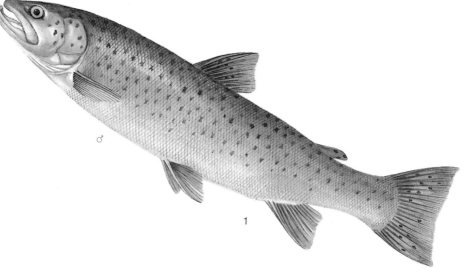

♂

1

Brown Trout
Salmo trutta m. *fario*
Salmonidae

This form of the Sea Trout is distributed in the central and mountain reaches of courses throughout the whole of Europe, the Caucasus, Asia Minor, Morocco and Algeria. It requires clean, cool water with a high oxygen content. As long as these conditions are fulfilled, it lives in suitable habitats from high mountain courses at altitudes of up to 2,000 m down to the valley reservoirs and cool ponds of the lowlands. In high mountain brooks which are poorly supplied with food it grows to a length of only 20-25 cm, in mountain rivers to about 35 cm, and in the lowlands, where feeding conditions are most favourable, it will attain a length of around 60 cm and a weight of 1-2 kg.

The Brown Trout is a territorial fish, inhabiting a specific part of a course for long periods, only mature fish leaving this briefly in the spawning season. The distance to the spawning grounds rarely exceeds 1 km. If there are rapids or waterfalls en route, it overcomes these by jumping. When jumping up it can reach speeds of up 37.2 km/hour and can jump over an obstacle as high as 1.5 m. It spawns from October until January in shallows with a sandy or gravelly bed. Using circular movements of the body, the female buries a proportion of the eggs in a previously prepared nest, stirring up a proportion of them, on the other hand, which drift downstream into crevices on the bottom. The greater part of these drifting eggs are, however, eaten by predatory fishes, including the Brown Trout itself. Its main diet, however, consists of insects, large individuals also devouring fishes, frogs, crayfish and small aquatic rodents.

The Brown Trout is one of the most important salmonid fish species in Europe. A method for artificial spawning which today ensures the survival of 80 per cent of the fry had already been developed in the 18th century.

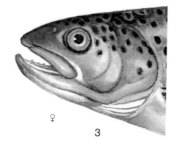

♀

3

The body of the Brown Trout (1) is streamlined and muscular, being adapted to life in flowing water. The powerfully toothed jaws indicate that this is a predatory fish. The caudal fin is

58

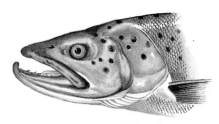

slightly indented only in young fish, old individuals having the rear edge even, as if stumped. The lower jaw of males (2) is bent into a hook shape. The head is elongated and slender. The female (3) has a shorter head with a roundish snout. The colouring of the Brown Trout varies considerably (4). Fish from shaded pools are dark, whilst those from sunlit courses are light. It is practically impossible to find two trout with the same colouring even in the same brook.

2 ♂

4

Lake Trout
Salmo trutta m. *lacustris*

Salmonidae

The lake form of the Sea Trout is proof of the great adaptability of trouts, which can even cope with the still waters of cool lakes and valley reservoirs.

The Lake Trout keeps predominantly to open water above the depths. Only the mature, 4-7-year-old fish swim to the shore in the period before spawning. In September and October they migrate en masse to the higher reaches of tributaries, where they lay their eggs into nests in the sand or gravel of the shallows. The adult fish return to the lakes after spawning, the young fish from the eggs remaining in the tributaries for 1-3 years, usually swimming out to the lakes at the beginning of summer. A proportion of the young fish, however, stay in the tributaries permanently and change into the Brown Trout form. Some young fish from the eggs of the Brown Trout, on the other hand, descend to lakes and develop into the lake form. The diet of the Lake Trout consists at first of small invertebrates and later predominantly of fishes. By virtue of the extensive size of its environment and often abundant food, it can grow very quickly. In an environment with a nutritious diet, it increases in size by 1-2 kg a year.

The Lake Trout is of greatest economic importance in Alpine lakes. In lowland areas its often occurs in low numbers, so its importance is restricted to localities with more numerous populations. It is a favourite angling fish.

Catches of the lake form of the Sea Trout (1) currently weigh 3-6 kg, although they can reach a size of 130 cm and a weight of 40 kg. A robust body with a high back and powerful tail indicate that it is a good swimmer.

It has a silverish colouring with an abundance of dark spots in the shape of the letter X or a small star. It does not have red spots, which are typical for the Brown Trout.

2

The female differs from the male in her finer head structure and shorter jaws.

The freshly hatched larvae of Salmonidae (2) obtain their nutrition from a large yolk-sac, which gradually shrinks, being used up after a month, so that the alevins have to look for food by themselves. The colour of the fish changes with age. Young fish (3), in contrast with adults, do not have spots on the body.

3

Atlantic Salmon
Salmo salar   Salmonidae

The Atlantic Salmon is a migratory fish. After reaching maturity at the age of 3-6 years it undertakes spawning migrations to the large rivers within its distribution — the European coast of the Arctic and Atlantic Oceans, the coast of Iceland, southern Greenland and the eastern part of North America. It also lives in the open sea, where it undertakes migrations for food as far as a distance of 1,300 km.

Spawning migration begins in June, when large-sized, sexually mature fish begin to appear in the rivers, followed in July by smaller fish, predominantly males. From the end of July until the beginning of September, fish with non-mature eggs and milt enter the rivers, not spawning until the following year. They do not take any food during migration. Their teeth enlarge, and in the case of males the lower jaw elongates and becomes even more bent into a hook. Spawning takes place in the upper reaches of rivers, upstream from the spawning grounds of trouts. The eggs are orange, and there are usually 6,000-40,000 of them. A proportion of the fish perish from exhaustion and injury shortly after spawning but the remainder return to the sea, still more of them perishing on the way. On the basis of spawning marks on the scales, ichtyologists have discovered that salmon spawn 2-5 times in a lifetime. Young fish remain in the rivers for varying lengths of time, depending on the geographical location of the spawning sites, this being up to 5 years in Norway, 2-5 years in England and only 1 year in the Rhine. Their diet consists predominantly of crustaceans, but large specimens hunt fishes. In the sea their prey include herring, sprats and mackerel.

The Atlantic Salmon is fished for in the sea, as well as during its migration in rivers, using the most diverse methods, which no doubt contributes to its declining.

4

Adult males (1) have the lower jaw bent into a hook and grow to a larger size than the females. The record for males is 150 cm, for females only 120 cm. Most Atlantic Salmon, however, measure 60-100 cm, weighing 15-20 kg.

Males turn dark during the period of sexual activity, red and pink spots appearing on the head and sides, the belly turning pink. Females (2) have light grey bodies with dark spots in the shape of the letter X or of a star. Young fish (3), the so-called parr, still living in fresh water, look more like trout. During the transition to the typical colouring of the adult fish, the red spots (4) disappear first. Salmon can be distinguished from trout by the arrangement of the gill bones. Whereas in Salmon (5) the four gill bones do not meet at a single point, in Trout they do (6).

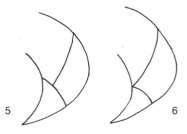

63

Rainbow Trout
Salmo gairdneri
Salmonidae

The Rainbow Trout used originally to inhabit the Pacific coast of North America and the rivers and lakes of this region. From here it was introduced to other regions of North America, and in 1875 to Europe (England) and later to other continents as well. Like the Sea Trout, the Rainbow Trout also occurs in a whole range of forms, depending on conditions, both in migratory sea and permanent fresh water ones. Nowadays it is the most widespread member of the family Salmonidae in Europe. It occurs both in the wild in valley reservoirs and their tributaries and in man-made structures, such as trout farms, ponds, and rearing cages. Its enormous adaptability to water temperature, oxygen content and dietary composition, as well as to water pollution, make it a fish with prospects for the future and in many places it is ousting the original Brown Trout species.

The reproduction of the Rainbow Trout generally falls within the same period as that of the Brown Trout, but in many populations it has shifted more to the spring season. The Rainbow Trout spawns in the upper reaches of courses from November until May. As with other trouts, the females construct nests on the bottom, in which they bury the 500-5,000 relatively large eggs, the development of which takes 100-150 days. The young fish feed on insects and their larvae, large specimens hunting mainly fishes. Males mature in their 2-3rd year, females not until the 3-5th year. Rainbow Trout normally live 5-8 years, exceptionally living to an age of 18 years or more. It is a sought-after fish species for anglers.

2

The characteristic feature of the permanent freshwater form of the Rainbow Trout (1) is the pink to reddish lengthwise band running along the middle of the body as far as the root of the tail. Its body shape resembles the Sea Trout, but it has a more robust body with larger scales, as well as fleshier meat and a smaller head. It normally grows to a length of up to 50 cm and 4-5 kg in weight, rarely up to 70 cm and 7 kg in weight. In its native habitat it

1

♀

♂

attains a greater size. Males differ from females by their longer head with the larger mouth, which has a longer, narrower lower jaw. Older males have the lower jaw bent into a hook. Some fish farms have managed to breed a golden form (2).

A systematic feature of salmonid fish is the vomer. The vomer in the Rainbow Trout (3—side view, 4—view from above) is longer than in the Brook Trout.

3

4

Charr
Salvelinus alpinus

Salmonidae

The Charr occurs in two forms within the area of its distribution. A migratory form lives in the Arctic seas of Europe, Asia, North America, and the coastal waters of Iceland, Spitzbergen and northern Norway, and a permanent freshwater form in the lakes of England, Ireland, Scotland, Finland, Sweden, Norway and in the Alpine lakes. In Alpine lakes it is a relic from the last Ice Age, occurring there up to altitudes of 2,400 metres. It enters tributaries in order to spawn.

The migratory form leaves the sea in September and October and swims into rivers. Spawning takes place from October to March in higher reaches over a gravelly bed. The female lays 560-7,300 eggs, with a diameter of 3-4 mm, among stones. The parental fish return to the sea after spawning. The young fish remain in fresh water, where they feed on the larvae of aquatic insects and insects which have dropped on to the surface. They hunt insects flying above the water by jumping, and larger specimens also eat small fishes. In the 3-4th year of its life, during the summer months, the Charr sets out downstream for the sea. In the sea, it feeds on fishes, predominantly herrings and small cods. When it matures in its 4-7th year, it migrates to rivers to spawn, thus completing the cycle.

The Charr is an economically significant species in Arctic waters, being fished for mainly in river estuaries during its spawning migrations. The lake forms are keenly fished for by sport fishermen.

The Charr (1) is the most colourful salmonid, the males being particularly brightly coloured. A striking feature is the contrast between the dark green colouring of the back and the orange-reddish belly. This contrast

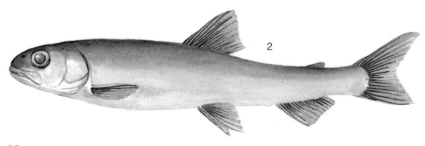

2

♀

1

♂

becomes even more marked during the period of spawning, when the back is greyish-blue and the belly reddish-orange. The females are smaller, having a finer head structure and less conspicuous colouring, which does change much during the spawning period. The Charr as a rule grows to a length of 40-60 cm and a weight of 1.5-3 kg. At the age of 10-12 years it can reach a size of up to 88 cm and a weight of 8-10 kg, but the migratory form is generally larger than the resident one. Some permanent lake populations (2) represent an extreme, and only attain a length of 10-18 cm.

The Charr (3) is easily distinguishable from the related Brook Trout (4) by the spacing and shape of vomer teeth.

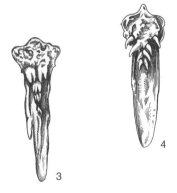

3

4

67

Brook Charr
Salvelinus fontinalis

Salmonidae

The Brook Charr was brought from America to Europe at the end of the last century, together with the Rainbow Trout. It was introduced into the lakes of England, Scandinavia, the Czech Republic, countries in the Alpine region and other places. In the course of time, it has disappeared from many localities, for example in England. A precondition for the occurrence of the Brook Charr is a low average water temperature, which should not exceed 16 °C during the year. It has thus survived only at higher elevations with clear, cool water. It inhabits both flowing water and lakes, in many localities together with the Brown Trout. As it can withstand even highly acidic water washed down from peat, and unlike the Brown Trout tolerates quite barren environments, it is often the only fish present under these conditions.

It spawns at the same time as the Brown Trout. When spawning, the two species often cross-breed. The cross-breeds are infertile and because of their special marbled colouring are known as tiger fish. The male and female of the Brook Charr bury 100-7,000 fertilized eggs in a bowl-like nest in the shallows of mountain torrents. The young fish feed mainly on insects, both aquatic ones and those taken from the surface. Larger individuals hunt fishes.

In North America in the Great Lakes region, the Brook Charr is the favourite species of sport fishermen. In European waters it is fished for using a rod and line, but with difficulty as it keeps predominantly to the depths of lakes, approaching the shore only at night. Its populations are low in numbers.

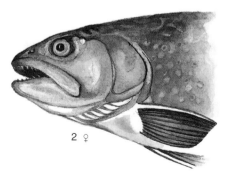

2 ♀

The Brook Charr (1), apart from the different arrangement of teeth on the vomer and its different colouring, differs from the Charr by its larger mouth. The upper jaw of the Charr extends at most to just behind the hind edge of the eye, whereas in the Brook Charr it extends much further. The male, as in other species of the *Salvelinus* genus, has a hook-shaped lower jaw. The female has a shorter head and a straight lower jaw, her upper jaw also extending far behind the hind edge of the eye (2). A characteristic feature of the species is the black colouring of the epithelium of the mouth.

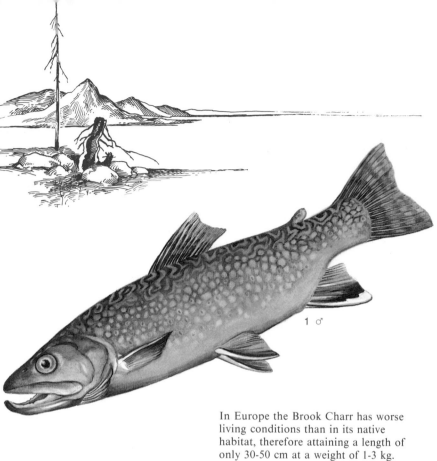

1 ♂

In Europe the Brook Charr has worse
living conditions than in its native
habitat, therefore attaining a length of
only 30-50 cm at a weight of 1-3 kg.
Conditions are particularly bad in high
mountain springs and in glacial lakes,
fish from these environments being
low-bodied, starved forms (3) with
conspicuously large heads.

3

Huchen
Hucho hucho

The Huchen is one of the most beautiful and largest salmonids, occurring at the margin between the grayling and barbel zones in the mountain and submontane reaches of the Danube and its tributaries. It has been introduced to other places, for example in the Czech Republic, from artificially bred stock, but survives successfully only in a few localities. In view of its size and territorial mode of life, it requires cool, clear, well-oxygenated water with plenty of hiding places.

The sexually mature, 4-6-year-old fish migrate upstream to spawn, in some places only several hundred metres, elsewhere migrating distances of up to several dozen kilometres. They seek out their spawning sites in shallow water with a gravelly or stony bed, spawning from March to May. The female beats out a large bowl-shaped nest in the bed, and, together with the male, covers the eggs with the bottom substrate during the spawning ritual. The number of eggs ranges from 2,000-25,000. The alevins feed on insects and their larvae, later also on the fry of other fish species. Larger Huchen are highly predatory, hunting fishes and small aquatic vertebrates. The fact that no other European predatory fish can devour such large quarry as the Huchen can in relation to the size of its body bears witness to its voraciousness. On account of its rich diet, the Huchen grows rapidly, growing in the first year to a size of up to 15 cm, and already measuring 40 cm and weighing 1 kg at the age of 2 $1/2$ years. Its meat has an excellent taste, its numbers, however, have dwindled as a result of intensive fishing.

The Huchen (1) has a slender cigar-shaped body. The broad mouth with its dense arrangement of teeth indicates that this is a powerful, predatory fish. Sexual differences between the male and female are negligible, the males having more vivid colouring, with the rear part of the belly dark pink only in the period of spawning. Females have silvery bellies.

1

2

3

The Huchen is the largest fish of the
Salmonidae family, often reaching
a weight of 5-10 kg. Nowadays, record
catches from the river Drava attain
weights of around 35 kg.

   Young Huchen differ markedly from
maturing fish by the transverse bands on
their sides, the so-called juvenile spots.
The colouring changes during the first
year of life, the juvenile spots
disappearing (2—Huchen at the age of
6 weeks, 3—at the age of 6 months,
4—at the age of 12 months).

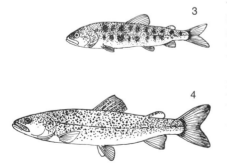

4

Humpback Salmon
Oncorhynchus gorbuscha

Salmonidae

The Humpback Salmon is the smallest, but at the same time the most important, species of the genus *Oncorhynchus*, sometimes known as the Pacific Salmons. It was introduced into the White Sea from the northern part of the Pacific Ocean and the Arctic Ocean, from where it has penetrated westwards towards the coast of Iceland, southern Norway, Scotland and northern England, as well as to the European rivers of this region. It is a migratory species, which leaves the sea in the second year of its life and enters rivers to spawn. The females bury the fertilized eggs in a previously prepared nest on the bottom and the exhausted fish of both sexes, injured by spawning, perish. The fry descend into the sea as quickly as possible after digesting the yolk-sac, feeding intensively there. By its 2nd year, the Humpback Salmon has already attained a length of 40-50 cm and weight of 1.5-2 kg, in exceptional cases growing up to a weight of 5 kg. It is of great economic significance. The pinkish meat, which has an excellent taste, is considered a delicacy.

The related Chum Salmon (*Oncorhynchus keta*) was also introduced to the White Sea from the Pacific and the Arctic Oceans. It penetrates European rivers to spawn, ascending further upstream than the Humpback Salmon, its spawning grounds being up to 3,500 km from the estuaries. They cover a daily distance of 40-85 km. According to the time of the spawning migration, it can be divided into two forms — summer and autumn ones. After spawning, the males leave the spawning site, whereas the females continue to protect the nest from other salmons for about another 10 days. During summer and autumn, the fry migrate to the sea, where they feed on fishes and crustaceans. The Chum Salmon grows to a length of 50-70 cm and a weight of 2-5 kg. In view of its rarity it is of no importance in European waters. It is fished for in Japan, the USA, the former USSR and Canada.

Pacific Salmons show a marked sexual dimorphism, which becomes even more pronounced at the time of sexual activity. The jaws of Humpback Salmon males (1) become excessively elongated and deformed in the period when the sexual products are maturing, a large fat hump also growing in front of the dorsal fin. The colouring also changes, being the same as that of the female outside the spawning period. The females (2) do not undergo such pronounced changes in the period of spawning activity. Their body morphology changes only by an increase in the size of the belly, which is filled with eggs, and by increased intensity of the original colouring.

1 ♂

2 ♀

3 ♂

4 ♀

Chum Salmon males (3) differ from females (4) both in body morphology and in their colouring. The body morphology and colouring of females do not change substantially whilst spawning, although a trace of the hook-like bending of the lower jaw does appear.

Freshwater Houting, Common Whitefish
Coregonus lavaretus
Coregonidae

The Freshwater Houting is the most widespread representative of the Coregonidae family in Europe, occurring in the river basins of the Baltic and North Seas and of the Arctic Ocean as far as the Kolyma river. A whole range of subspecies occurs, which further subdivide into many local forms. Sexually mature, 3-4-year-old fish take part in spawning migrations, entering the lower reaches of rivers from the coast. The river populations migrate upstream to higher reaches, whilst part of the lake populations spawn in deeper lakes, and part migrate to their tributaries. The Freshwater Houting is of great economic significance. It is fished for using both nets and traps, in central and eastern Europe being introduced into ponds as an auxiliary fish species to carp. As it does not reproduce naturally in ponds, its numbers have to be made up from artificial spawning.

The Vendace or Cisco (*Coregonus albula*) grows in several forms. In Ladoga Lake, where it has sufficient food (mainly Chironomid larvae), it attains a weight of up to 1.2 kg. This large growth form has been introduced into other European regions, although it has not held its own in many places. In waters poorly supplied with food, the Vendace grows slowly, measuring only 8 cm at the age of 2-3 years, when it attains sexual maturity. The Vendace occurs in lakes with cool water in the river-basins of the Baltic and White Seas, in the river-basin of the upper Volga, in Norway, Denmark, and in northern Germany in most lakes east of the Elbe. It is fished for using hunting nets, dragnets and fish-pots.

The Freshwater Houting (1) grows very quickly, usually attaining a length of about 60 cm and a weight of about 3 kg. Isolated catches can measure up to 130 cm and weigh up to 10 kg. It has an elongated, laterally-flattened body and a small head. The short snout is steeply slanting, and the ventral mouth is toothless. The small adipose fin between the dorsal and caudal fin is a characteristic feature of the family, as is also the case in Salmonid species.

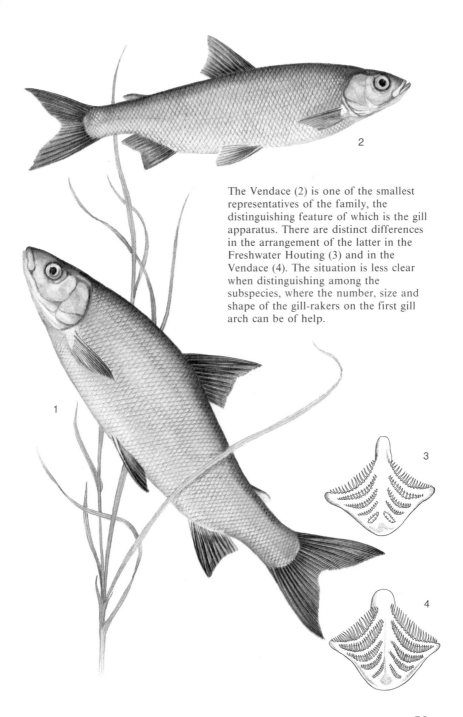

The Vendace (2) is one of the smallest representatives of the family, the distinguishing feature of which is the gill apparatus. There are distinct differences in the arrangement of the latter in the Freshwater Houting (3) and in the Vendace (4). The situation is less clear when distinguishing among the subspecies, where the number, size and shape of the gill-rakers on the first gill arch can be of help.

Siberian Cisco, Peled
Coregonus peled

Coregonidae

The Siberian Cisco originally inhabited the rivers and lakes feeding the Arctic Ocean from the river Mezen in the west as far as the Kolyma in the east. In central and northern Europe, where it has been introduced, it is bred mainly in ponds. Fish there reach a weight of 1 kg when they are only 3 years old. In open waters it lives mainly in lakes. Some populations migrate to rivers early in spring to spawn. Other populations are permanent and spawn in lakes. Sexual activity in the Siberian Cisco manifests itself in the growth of a spawning rash, not only in males, but often also in females. The spawning sites are on stony or sandy substrates. The eggs are yellow, and usually there are 3,000-125,000 of them. The Siberian Cisco matures in its 5-6th year, in the ponds of central Europe as early as the 2nd year, feeding on zooplankton and small crustaceans, and lives up to 10 years. It is of great economic significance and is proving to have a whole range of useful biological and productive characteristics for fish-pond keeping. It grows rapidly, matures early, and will withstand fluctuations in temperature and low oxygen content in water, as well as handling when being transported. These are all characteristics which make it a fish species with good breeding prospects.

The Tshiir or Broad Whitefish (*Coregonus nasus*) is distributed in the river-basins of the Arctic Ocean from the Petchora to the Chukotski peninsula, as well as in Alaska and Canada. It inhabits lakes and the lower reaches of rivers, penetrating even to brackish waters. It occurs in many forms, which differ from one another in their biology. By virtue of its large size and abundance, it is an important fishing species.

The Siberian Cisco (1) is a high-bodied fish with large eyes and a terminal mouth. In large specimens, the back is raised in a steep arch, forming a hump. It usually grows to a length of up to 60 cm and a weight of 2.5-3 kg in weight. In isolated cases, specimens

3

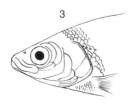

4

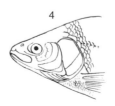

5

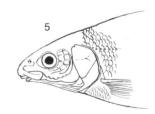

have been observed in the Yenisei weighing up to 5 kg.

The Tshiir (2) is one of the largest representatives of the family, in Siberia in the Kolyma attaining a weight of up to 16 kg, otherwise being similar to the Siberian Cisco in size.

The position of the mouth is an important systematic feature of the Coregonidae family. The Siberian Pygmy Marane (*Coregonus sardinella*) has a dorsal mouth (3). The Arctic Cisco (*Coregonus autumnalis*) has a terminal mouth (4), the same as the Siberian Cisco. The Freshwater Houting (*Coregonus lavaretus*) has a ventral mouth (5) similar to that, for example, of the Tshiir.

Houting
Coregonus oxyrhynchus
Coregonidae

The Houting is distributed along the south and south-east coast of the North Sea, along the west coast of the Baltic Sea, in the great lakes of southern Sweden and some Alpine lakes. Within most of its distribution it is represented by a migratory form, which inhabits both the sea and brackish waters. The migratory form enters fresh river waters in autumn to spawn. The permanent freshwater form occurs in Swedish and Alpine lakes and in the basin of the river Schlei in Germany. The migratory form spawns from October to December on the sandy or gravelly bed of the lower reaches of rivers. After hatching, the fry swim out to sea, where they feed intensively and mature in their 3rd or 4th year. The diet of the young fish consists of minute planktonic fauna, mainly crustaceans, larger fish gathering mainly bottom fauna (benthos). Serious river pollution has rendered reproduction completely impossible for the migratory form of the Houting, thus causing such a decline in its numbers that it is nowadays on the verge of extinction.

The Smelt (*Osmerus eperlanus*), belonging to the family Osmeridae, differs from members of the Coregonidae, Salmonidae and Thymallidae families in that its stomach consists of a blind sac. It inhabits the waters of the northern hemisphere, also occurring in a permanent freshwater form apart from the migratory sea form. The migratory form spawns in rivers. The numbers of Smelt fluctuate greatly, depending on the conditions for the survival of the fry. When the conditions are propitious, a mass migration (a so-called Smelt year), which is of course exploited for intensive fishing, takes place after 3-4 years, when the young fish from the spawning reach maturity.

The Houting (1) grows to a length of 25-40 cm, and a weight of about 1 kg. It is one of the larger members of the family, as is proved by record catches of fish 50 cm long and weighing 2 kg. The tiny, toothless mouth (2), concealed underneath the head under the elongated snout, bears witness to the fact that the Houting seeks food in the bottom sediments.

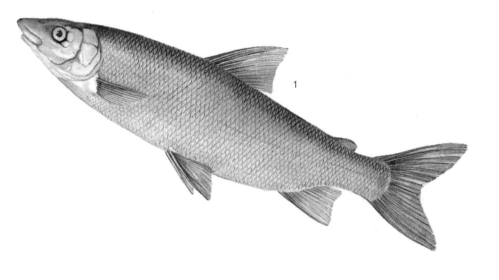

The Smelt (3) is a small fish. Its freshwater form grows slowly, attaining a size of 10-15 cm, at most 20 cm, whilst the migratory form attains a length of 15-18 cm, in rare cases 30 cm. Smelt fry (4) are a copy of the mature fish on a smaller scale, the most important features, such as the small adipose fin, the shape of the caudal fin, the shape of the dorsal fin and the position of the mouth being preserved. This facilitates differentiation of Smelt fry from those of related families — Coregonidae, Salmonidae and Thymallidae.

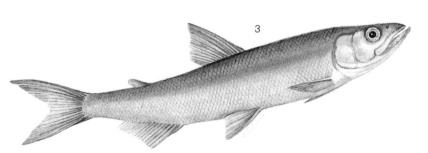

Grayling
Thymallus thymallus   Thymallidae

The Grayling is distributed throughout most European countries, eastwards as far as the Urals, westwards as far as Wales and France and southwards as far as northern Italy. It inhabits mountain and submontane streams with clear, cool and well-oxygenated water, and prefers an environment with pools and hiding places under the banks. It can nevertheless also be found in suitable uniform waters with clean, gravelly or sandy beds, but above all prefers places where slow currents above pools alternate with rapids. Grayling are the typical fishes for these waters, the reaches in which they occur being known as the grayling zone in angling terminology. Apart from these typical swift reaches, the Grayling also inhabits cool North European lakes, bays in the Baltic Sea along the coast of Sweden and Finland and occasionally even brackish water.

The Grayling spawns en masse from March to May on a sandy or gravelly bed at depths of about 50 cm. The males beat out nests in the bottom and the females bury the fertilized eggs in them. The spawned eggs are guarded and protected by the males, which are conspicuous with their intensive colouring during the spawning season, especially with the contrast between the blue and red colouring on the dorsal fin. The Grayling feeds mainly on insects and their larvae, larger specimens also on young fishes, for example Minnows. Grayling silently hunt insects flying down to the water-surface. They rise from the depths to the surface, seizing them without even making a smacking sound and diving silently towards the bottom. Only there is the quarry swallowed, even if it is only a tiny fly.

The Grayling (1) has a slender, elongated body with a small adipose fin on the peduncle. The head is small, with a ventral mouth equipped with small teeth. A conspicuous feature is the large, flag-like dorsal fin, which is striking mainly in the males. Females have a lower dorsal fin, less conspicuous colouring, and are stouter in the period prior to spawning. Grayling catches are around 30 cm and 250 g, rarely reaching 50 cm and 1 kg.

2

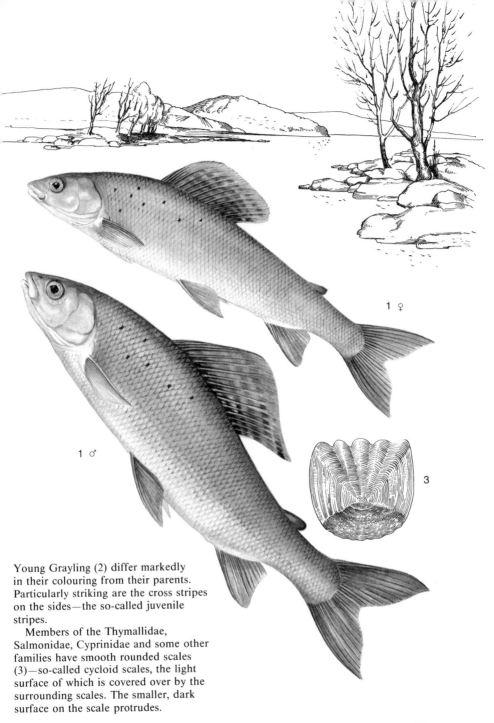

1 ♀

1 ♂

3

Young Grayling (2) differ markedly
in their colouring from their parents.
Particularly striking are the cross stripes
on the sides—the so-called juvenile
stripes.

Members of the Thymallidae,
Salmonidae, Cyprinidae and some other
families have smooth rounded scales
(3)—so-called cycloid scales, the light
surface of which is covered over by the
surrounding scales. The smaller, dark
surface on the scale protrudes.

81

Mudminnow
Umbra krameri
Umbridae

The Mudminnow was at one time an abundant species within the Danube river-basin from Vienna as far as its estuary and in the lower reaches of the Dnieper and the Prut. In recent years, however, it has entirely disappeared from many localities, for example from the Balaton and Neusiedler lakes. Its numbers have also declined considerably elsewhere, the reason for this being the drainage of flood-prone territories, the canalisation of courses and water pollution. The typical habitat of the Mudminnow consists of irrigation canals, blind river arms, and the pools and marshes of flood-prone territory with dense aquatic plant cover, all of which provide it with refuge and protection from predatory fishes. By means of auxiliary respiration — swallowing air from the surface — the Mudminnow can overcome the unfavourable heat of summer, when many of these biotopes dry out.

The Mudminnow usually spawns only once in a lifetime, as only a small proportion of the population survives until the next spawning. It spawns from March to May. The female excavates a shallow pit in the sandy bottom using circular movements of the body. She is highly aggressive and drives off both the male and other fishes. Together with 2-3 males, she deposits in the nest 100-120 viscous eggs, in which there are oily drops. The male becomes pale and sickly after spawning, whereas the female on the other hand becomes even more intensively coloured, and becomes aggressive once again, protecting and taking care of the spawn, often until the embryos hatch. The Mudminnow is a short-lived fish. It hunts food by darting, which is preceded by a phase of inconspicuous, gradual approach. Nowadays it is such a rare fish that it is a protected species in many countries.

The Mudminnow (1) has a short, stout body at most 13 cm long. The scales fall off easily and also intrude upon the upper part and sides of the head. There are small teeth in the mouth which grow not only on the jaws, but also on other bones in the oral cavity. The lateral line is discernible as a light stripe on the sides, although it lacks the typical small apertures in the scales. The Mudminnow is able to move its paired fins alternately

3

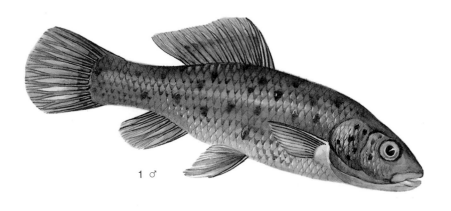

1 ♂

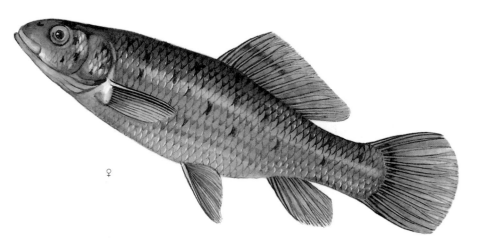

♀

and independently of each other, so that its locomotion is reminiscent of a running dog (2). This is also the reason why 200 years ago it was described as the 'Dog Goby' — *Gobius caninus.*

The Eastern Mudminnow (*Umbra pygmaea*) (3) does not differ substantially in its biology from the Mudminnow. From the eastern part of the USA, it was sporadically introduced into some countries of western Europe, growing to a maximum length of 12 cm.

2

83

Pike
Esox lucius

Esocidae

The Pike inhabits waters throughout the whole of Europe with the exception of southern peninsulas and Norway, and also north Asia and North America. It is a typical inhabitant of gently-flowing and still, overgrown waters with backwaters and side river arms with hiding places. It lives both in lowland warm waters and in gently-flowing submontane rivers. It spawns in March and April, sometimes even under the ice at water temperatures of 5-12 °C. It spawns exclusively amongst plants, for example on flooded meadows, and in places where vegetation is lacking it does not spawn. The eggs have a viscous cover and adhere to plants. Their number depends on the size of the female (from 10,000 to 50,000 eggs). It is sometimes spawned artificially with the intention of maintaining its numbers in open waters.

The Pike is a typical territorial predator lying in wait in a hiding-place for its quarry. It gains information about its quarry both from its large eyes and the sensory cells in small pits on the head and in the lateral line. The sharp back-pointing teeth on the jaws and palate give the quarry little hope of escape. Only larger, high-bodied fishes can succeed, such as for example the Bream. The teeth do not serve for cutting, but for gripping the quarry and pushing it into the oesophagus with alternate movements of the upper and lower jaw. The powerful juices of the digestive system can digest not only a captured fish, but also the steel of a hook, spoon or stranded wire. The Pike grows quickly, catches commonly measuring 1 m and weighing 5-12 kg.

The Pike is a favourite fish of anglers. It is introduced into ponds as an auxiliary fish to the Carp, where it weeds out unwanted fishes.

2

84

The Pike body (1) is perfectly adapted to lightning-fast acceleration as it darts at its quarry. The cylindrical cross-section of the body and shifting of the unpaired fins towards the end of the body enables it to produce great speed over a short distance simply by moving the rear parts of its body. The wide-open mouth with the cage of the expanded gill arches ensures a fast through flow of water during the attack. The great expandability of the jaws, gill arches and belly enable it to swallow even a fish which has a higher body than the Pike itself.

The young fish (2) is noted for its slender, low body. The freshly hatched larva (3) is attached to a plant by means of the viscous larval organ on its forehead. The nutrition of the 10 mm long larva (4) is ensured by the yolk-sac. The fry, which are 13 mm in size, already hunt minute zooplankton.

85

Roach
Rutilus rutilus

Cyprinidae

The Roach is one of the most common fish species in European waters, being absent only on southern peninsulas and in the greater part of Norway. It occurs in the deeper reaches of rivers with slowly flowing water, in blind river arms, in lowland lakes, ponds and valley reservoirs, in isolated cases reaching as far as trout waters. A migratory form lives in the brackish water of the Baltic, Black, Aral and Caspian Seas.

From February to April at temperatures above 10 °C mass spawning takes place. Roach spawn in shallow overgrown reaches near the banks at depths of up to 1.5 m. The female lays 1,000-100,000 eggs, this being the reason why Roach are so numerous. The fry hatch in 4-10 days; after digesting the yolk-sac they change over to an active method of obtaining food. The migratory form enters rivers from brackish waters to spawn. Since this form attains a larger size, the females lay up to 200,000 eggs. The Roach is omnivorous, eating predominantly zooplankton, as well as insects, their larvae and molluscs, but plants and detritus are also taken.

The migratory form of the Roach is exploited economically in Poland and the former USSR, where it is fished for and its meat processed industrially. In inland waters the Roach is not economically important, although it is popular with anglers. In some ponds and waterworks reservoirs it is considered an undesirable species, which often over-reproduces, individuals becoming stunted. In view of its small size and large numbers, it forms a basic component of the diet of many predatory fishes.

2

The Roach (1) has a medium high, flat-sided body and a terminal mouth. A striking feature is the red eye, the upper half of which is deep coloured. The dorsal fin lies above the base of the ventral fins, being pinkish-grey, as are the caudal and pectoral fins. The anal and ventral fins are orange red. It differs in the above-mentioned features from the similar Rudd. It commonly grows to a length of 30-35 cm and 0.5 kg in weight, record catches reaching up to 2.1 kg in weight.

1

3

The viscous eggs attach themselves to the fine roots of bankside growth, soft aquatic plant growth, and occasionally to small twigs (2). In dams with dumped stony banks and insufficient growth the Roach spawns on sharp stony debris (3). As a result of vigorous spawning, many fish are so grazed on the stones that they bleed.

Danube Roach
Rutilus pigus

Cyprinidae

The Danube Roach occurs in two subspecies, one living in the Danube and its river-basin, the other in northern Italy. It inhabits slowly flowing, deeper river reaches, pools and blind river arms. In April and May it spawns in overgrown bankside shallows. The fecundity of the female is up to 60,000 eggs, which are viscous and attach themselves to plants and stones on the bottom. In the period of sexual activity the males are easily distinguished from the females. Like most members of the family Cyprinidae, males have a spawning rash, which appears in this species not only on the head, back and sides, but also on the fins, including the caudal fin. The diet of the fry consists of minute zooplankton, larger fish-eating small bottom fauna, mainly molluscs, worms and crustaceans, and to some extent also plants. This species reaches sexual maturity in 2-3 years, at a size of up to 20 cm. It grows to lengths of up to 40 cm and 1 kg in weight.

It is of little economic significance. It is rarely fished for industrially, and then only inadvertently whilst fishing for other more important species. From time to time it is fished for by anglers.

2 ♂

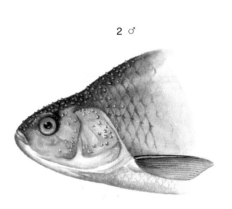

The Danube Roach (1) has, in comparison with the Roach, a more slender and longer body, a dark green back and yellowish-orange eyes. The inner epithelium of the abdominal cavity is black. The large scales have an opalescent sheen.

The differences between the male and female in roaches are negligible, with the exception of the period of sexual activity, when males develop small epidermal papillae, the so-called spawning rash (2) on the head, back, sides and sometimes even on the fins. Sporadically and in quite small numbers, the rash also occurs in females. After spawning, the rash disappears.

The position of the dorsal fin is an
important systematic feature which
facilitates distinguishing roaches from
similar species of other members of the
Cyprinidae family, for example the
Rudd. In roaches, the dorsal fin grows
above the base of the ventral fins (3).

89

Black Sea Roach, Pearl Roach
Rutilus frisii

Cyprinidae

The Black Sea Roach is widespread in Alpine lakes along the upper course of the Danube (Chiemsee, Traunsee, Attersee, Mondsee) and in their tributaries, as well as in the Black Sea and the Sea of Azov, including the tributaries in the north-west part and in the Caspian Sea and its tributaries.

Lake populations migrate to the tributaries or upper reaches of the Danube to spawn, where they seek out stony places with clear, cool, swiftly flowing water in the central part of the river bed. From April to May they spawn either among the plant growth or on the gravelly bottom. Spawning shoals consist of fish with a minimum age of 3-6 years and a weight greater than 1 kg. The fecundity of the females reaches up to 256,000 eggs. Spawning migrations of populations from brackish waters take place both in spring and autumn. The autumn population overwinters in the lower reaches of rivers, ascending into central reaches, where it spawns, in early spring. The spring form enters rivers after the ice has started to break up, taking part in spawning immediately after its arrival at the spawning grounds. After spawning, the fish return to brackish waters, the freshwater forms to lakes. The Black Sea Roach lives on minute animals, to some extent also on fragments of plants and small fishes. It is fished for mainly in the region of the Black and Caspian Seas and the Sea of Azov, most frequently in rivers in the period of spawning migrations, using both nets and the rod and line.

In the rivers of Italy and in the basins of rivers which flow into the Adriatic Sea, the related *Rutilus rubilio* is an abundant species, inhabiting mainly slowly-flowing and still waters. In spite of its relatively small size — it measures only 20-25 cm, at most 30 cm — it is of local importance both for fishermen fishing with nets and for anglers.

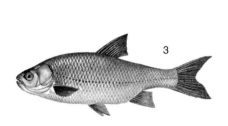

The Black Sea Roach (1) has an elongate body with large, silvery shiny scales. It normally grows to a length of 40-50 cm and a weight of 1-2 kg. A record catch measured 71 cm, weighing 6 kg. The spawning rash on the body of males, unlike in most species, does not appear just before spawning, but in autumn, rarely even at the end of the summer.

1 ♂

Rutilus frisii forms three subspecies within the area of its distribution. In Alpine lakes and the upper reach of the Danube lives *Rutilus frisii meidingeri*, in the Black Sea and the Sea of Azov and their tributaries *Rutilus frisii frisii* (2), the Caspian Sea and the area that feeds it being inhabited by *Rutilus frisii kutum*.

Rutilus rubilio (3) is smaller than the above-mentioned species, having a higher, shorter body covered with large silvery scales.

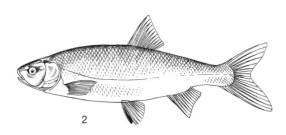

2

Dace
Leuciscus leuciscus
Cyprinidae

The Dace is distributed throughout the whole of Europe, with the exception of Scotland, northern Scandinavia and southern peninsulas. It inhabits the swift reaches of brooks, torrents and rivers from the trout zone as far as the bream zone. It swims in small groups, mainly near the bottom, where it eats insects and their larvae, molluscs, fish eggs, fry and to a lesser extent also plant fragments. Towards evening and at night it swims up to the surface, where it hunts insects which have fallen on to the surface. In muddy water, it likes to collect earthworms which have been washed into the water after rains.

It starts to spawn in the third and fourth year of its life, spawning from March to May in overgrown shallows with current. In cool waters it spawns later, sometimes not until June, depositing eggs on plants and their underwashed roots or directly on to the stony bottom. Unlike most fishes, which migrate to higher reaches to spawn, the Dace descends from the trout and grayling zones to lower reaches. In the breeding season the male can be distinguished by the spawning rash on its head, body and paired fins. The female lays 2,500-27,500 eggs 2 mm in diameter. After hatching and digesting the yolk-sac, the fry throng in large shoals. As the fish gradually grow older, however, the shoals decrease in size until they disintegrate into a large number of small groups.

The Dace is not a particularly abundant species, its meat moreover being of low quality with many intermuscular bones. It is occasionally fished for by anglers, most often using an artificial fly.

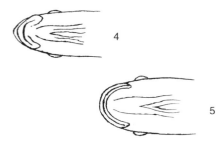

The Dace (1) is a slender fish with relatively large scales. Unlike in the similar Chub, the scales are a uniform colour, without dark bordering. It normally grows to a length of 20-25 cm, weighing 200 g. A record fish caught in England measured 30 cm and weighed 570 g.

The Dace has a small ventral mouth, which is somewhat further away from the snout (2). The related Chub (3) has a broad mouth at the end of the snout.

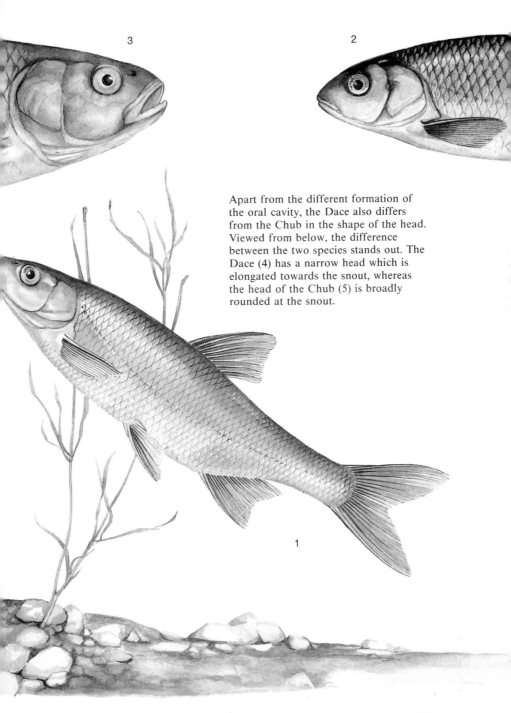

3

2

Apart from the different formation of the oral cavity, the Dace also differs from the Chub in the shape of the head. Viewed from below, the difference between the two species stands out. The Dace (4) has a narrow head which is elongated towards the snout, whereas the head of the Chub (5) is broadly rounded at the snout.

1

Chub
Leuciscus cephalus

Cyprinidae

Apart from Ireland, northern Scandinavia and islands in the Mediterranean Sea, the Chub inhabits the whole of Europe, living in fresh as well as brackish waters, such as the Baltic Sea. Despite its great capacity for adaptation to all water types, the Chub has a marked preference for flowing water with a hard bed. In lowland rivers it often keeps downstream from weirs, as well as under sewage outlets, where it feeds on the waste. In trout waters it is an unwelcome species that competes with trout for food, moreover also eating their eggs and alevins. The Chub is highly voracious, feeding both on plant and animal food. Large individuals will hunt fishes, frogs and crayfish, and will even take fruit that has fallen into the water. In spite of this, however, the Chub grows relatively slowly.

It spawns in spring. At this time the males, and more rarely even females, have a spawning rash on the body and head, the males also having bright red anal and ventral fins. The females lay 50,000-200,000 eggs in several batches. After digesting the yolk-sac, the fry intensively hunt minute zooplankton. Young Chub keep in shoals, whilst older fish live solitarily. They keep just under the surface, therefore registering every danger. The Chub is very shy, this being particularly true of older fish.

It has no special economic importance, despite being abundant. From the ecological viewpoint it could, thanks to its adaptability, replace species declining as a result of pollution or damage to their environment.

The Chub (1) is a robust, cylindrical-shaped fish with a large broad head and a wide terminal mouth. The scales are large with dark borders. It usually grows to a length of 40-45 cm and a weight of 0.5-1 kg, sporadically growing to 60-70 cm and 3-4 kg. A record catch from the Dniestr measured 80 cm and weighed 8 kg.

A significant distinguishing feature of the family is the shape of the anal fin. The Chub (2) has a broad anal fin with a convex edge, that of the Dace (3) being narrow and concave and that of the Ide (4) being broad and concave.

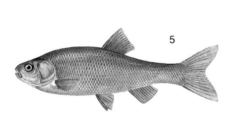

5

In the torrents and lakes of south-west
Balkan peninsula lives the related Makal Dace
(*Leuciscus microlepis*) (5), a small fish
growing to a length of only 20-30 cm.

95

Ide, Orfe
Leuciscus idus

Cyprinidae

The Ide is distributed in Europe from the Rhine to the Urals, being absent in the north of the British Isles, France, Switzerland, Norway and in the region south of the Alps and the Danube. It inhabits the central and lower reaches of rivers, valley reservoirs and lakes. It has also been introduced as a secondary species into some ponds, river arms and sand-pits. It prefers deeper, gently flowing water, where it lives in large shoals which hunt food near the bottom. In the spring it migrates en masse to the spawning sites, where it spawns in pairs from April to June. It takes up to 3 days for a pair to spawn and the spawning is a markedly vigorous affair. The female deposits up to 114,000 eggs on aquatic plants or the fine roots of underwashed bankside growth. As in the majority of Cyprinidae, a spawning rash appears on the body of Ides at the time of spawning, being more pronounced in males, and both sexes turn an intense golden colour. Initially the fry live on minute zooplankton, more grown-up fish on smaller insect larvae. Large individuals hunt insects and fishes. They reach maturity between their 3rd and 5th year, living up to 15 years, and generally attain a length of 35-50 cm and a weight of 2 kg. A record catch measured 47 cm and weighed 4.7 kg. The Ide is a popular fish among anglers, as catching it requires considerable experience. It has yellowish, tasty meat.

In the Cetina river-basin of Dalmatia lives the related Ukliva Dace (*Leuciscus ukliva*), and in the torrents and lakes of the Narenta river-basin another related species, Turskyi Dace (*Leuciscus turskyi*) occurs. Both these species live on minute invertebrates, mainly worms, crustaceans and insect larvae.

In contrast with the preceding species, the Ide (1) has a markedly high body, reminiscent of the Roach. Unlike in the Roach, however, the beginning of its dorsal fin is behind the perpendicular line raised from the bases of the ventral fins. The golden form of the Ide,

3

4

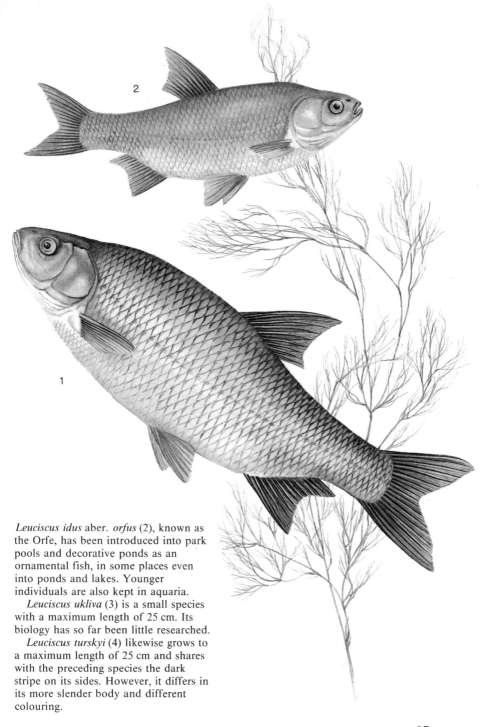

Leuciscus idus aber. *orfus* (2), known as the Orfe, has been introduced into park pools and decorative ponds as an ornamental fish, in some places even into ponds and lakes. Younger individuals are also kept in aquaria.

Leuciscus ukliva (3) is a small species with a maximum length of 25 cm. Its biology has so far been little researched.

Leuciscus turskyi (4) likewise grows to a maximum length of 25 cm and shares with the preceding species the dark stripe on its sides. However, it differs in its more slender body and different colouring.

Souffie
Leuciscus souffia

Cyprinidae

The Souffie only occurs in central Europe and in the river-basins of the Rhine, the Rhone, the Po and the Danube. It inhabits mainly the tributaries of the upper and central reaches of the above-mentioned rivers and also some Alpine lakes, where it ascends to altitudes of up to 2,000 m.

The Souffie is a gregarious fish, shoaling in gently-flowing places away from the mainstream. It gathers in shallow currents with a stony or gravelly bed to spawn. In the period of spawning from March to May, a spawning rash appears on the head and body in both sexes, although being less extensive in the female. The female lays 5,500-8,000 eggs on the stones of the bottom. It has the same spawning site requirements as the Nase. Since the spawning period also coincides in both species, they often spawn together, hybrids sometimes being produced.

The Souffie feeds on small bottom-dwelling invertebrates. It also likes to gather insects which have fallen on to the surface. In lakes it lives at greater depths, therefore hunting plankton instead of insects flying near the surface. It grows to a length of only 12-18 cm, rarely up to 25 cm, and a weight of 50-70 g. On account of its low numbers and small size, it is of no economic use. Anglers use it as bait.

The Souffie (1) is a small slender fish with a body elongated into a cylindrical shape. A striking feature is the dark blue to black stripe on its side. The colouring is especially intense during the spawning period, when the Souffie has a dark bluish-violet back and a creamy-white belly, ranking on account of its colouring among the most beautiful Cyprinidae fishes.

The species *Leuciscus svallize* (2) attains the same size as the Souffie. It inhabits only the clean torrents and swift-flowing rivers of south-west Balkan peninsula. The biology of its reproduction is unknown. It is of local economic importance.

3

The species *Leuciscus illyricus* (3) lives in the most diverse types of water in western Balkan peninsula. It does not differ in size from the previous two species. This is a little researched species, although being of a certain economic significance. It is fished for using both nets and rods.

2

1

Minnow
Phoxinus phoxinus
Cyprinidae

The Minnow is distributed throughout the whole of Europe with the exception of northern Scotland, the greater part of Ireland, northern Scandinavia, southern Spain and Portugal, and central and southern Italy.

It inhabits torrents, small rivers and lakes with cool, well-oxygenated water. It is a gregarious fish, spending the whole of its life in a shoal. For the purposes of maintaining contact among the fishes of the shoal, there are special club-like mucoid cells scattered in the epidermis and excreting mucus with a characteristic smell. The fish constantly smell this, thus being able to keep together, even at night or in muddy water when sight is useless. Only when attacked by a predator does the shoal flee in all directions with lightning speed and the Minnows seek refuge in bankside shallows among stones close to the bank, where because of the shallow water not even trout can reach them. As soon as the danger has passed the minnows return to the shoal.

In May and July the Minnow shoals concentrate for spawning in the shallow, flowing parts of courses. There the female sticks the 200-2,000 eggs on the stones or gravel of the bottom. The large number of eggs for such a small fish compensates for the great losses incurred by trout and other predatory fish.

The Minnow is highly sensitive to water pollution. Nowadays the number of places in which it still occurs has greatly reduced. It is an important dietary item for trouts, otherwise not being of any particular significance.

The Minnow (1) has a spindle-shaped body with rounded fins. It usually grows to a length of 6-10 cm, rarely to 14 cm. It only has scales on its sides, these being tiny and almost invisible. It feeds on small aquatic insects, for which it rises to the surface, but also on small fauna living on the bottom or in vegetation growing in the current. The increased level of sexual hormones in breeding season causes striking differences between the male (2) and female (3). The male is more slender and conspicuously brightly coloured, especially with red on the belly. Viewed from above, he has protruding, thick opercula. On the head he has

3 ♀

1

2 ♂

a pronounced light-coloured spawning
rash.

The Minnow ranks among the most
beautiful European freshwater fishes.
The female is stout, less brightly
coloured and has a less obvious
spawning rash.

Swamp Minnow
Phoxinus percnurus

Cyprinidae

The Swamp Minnow is distributed throughout eastern Europe and the river-basins of rivers feeding the Arctic Ocean. It prefers the still waters of lakes, pools and areas flooded by rivers, where it seeks out shallows richly covered with vegetation. It sometimes inhabits the extreme conditions of muddy and warmed-up waters in which a stunted form of the Crucian Carp is the only other species to survive. It can withstand a shortage of oxygen, a fact which markedly distinguishes it from the related Minnow.

Swamp Minnows spawn in the period from May to July, the egg-laying taking place in several batches and the total number of eggs ranging from 1,600 to 18,700. The eggs are viscous and adhere to aquatic plants. The larvae hatch after 5-8 days, hiding among plants for the first few days. To enable them to live in an environment short of oxygen they are equipped with auxiliary external gills behind the gills proper — known as larval respiration organs. These disappear as the yolk-sac is digested and the larvae change into fry. The Swamp Minnow reaches maturity in its 2nd-3rd year. Its diet consists of invertebrates, mainly worms, insect larvae, flying insects and to some extent even aquatic plants.

From the economic viewpoint, the Swamp Minnow is only of local importance as a food, additionally serving as bait for anglers.

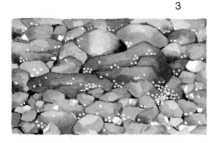

3

Unlike the Minow, which has an elongate, spindle-shaped body, the Swamp Minnow (1) is a stout, high-bodied fish reminiscent of the Tench in its body shape and to some extent also in its colouring. It usually grows to a length of 8-15 cm, rarely 19 cm, and a weight of up to 100 g.

This different body shape and biology are the result of the different environments in which the two minnows live. The Swamp Minnow spawns on aquatic plant growth in still waters (2), the Minnow on the stony bed of currents (3).

Rudd
Scardinius erythrophthalmus

Cyprinidae

The Rudd inhabits North Asia and Europe with the exception of the greater part of Scandinavia, northern Scotland, the Pyrenees, and part of the Apennine and Balkan peninsulas, also being absent from European islands. It lives predominantly in lowland, slow-flowing waters, but also inhabits the still waters of dams, ponds, blind river arms, pools and lakes in former sand quarries. It prefers densely over-grown territories, where it keeps to the vicinity of banks. On warm sunny days it will rise in shoals to the surface. It spawns in May and June amongst aquatic plants in clean still water. The female deposits 80,000-200,000 viscous eggs in 2 batches on to the plants. The fry hatch after 3-10 days, lying passively hidden in the growth until they have digested the yolk-sac. The Rudd is one of the few members of the family Cyprinidae which takes food the whole year round, apart from the short spawning period. Small fish feed on plankton, larger ones mainly on plant food, as well as insects, molluscs and fish fry. The Rudd is an adaptable species. In some densely overgrown and highly acid old river arms it is often one of the last remaining species surviving in these unfavourable conditions. It forms an important component in the diet of predatory fishes.

The subspecies *Scardinius erythrophthalmus racovitzai* has adapted to extreme conditions for fish life, living in the hot springs of western Romania. The optimum temperature range for this subspecies is 28-34 °C. It perishes at temperatures below 20 °C.

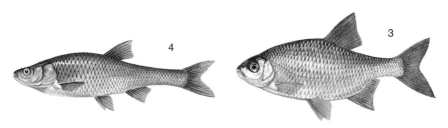

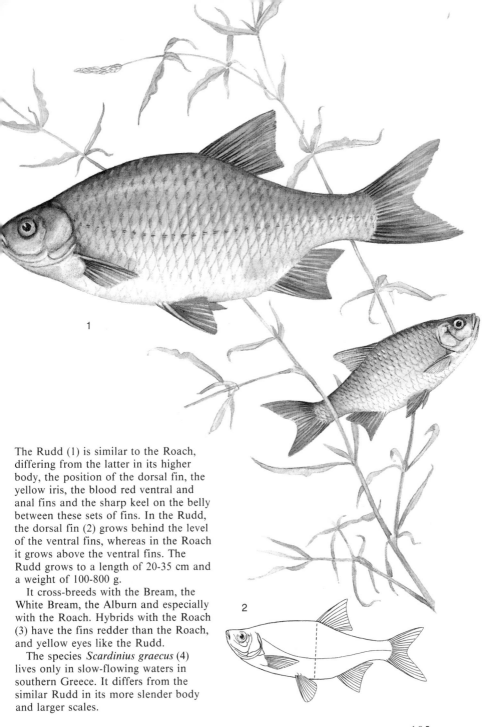

The Rudd (1) is similar to the Roach, differing from the latter in its higher body, the position of the dorsal fin, the yellow iris, the blood red ventral and anal fins and the sharp keel on the belly between these sets of fins. In the Rudd, the dorsal fin (2) grows behind the level of the ventral fins, whereas in the Roach it grows above the ventral fins. The Rudd grows to a length of 20-35 cm and a weight of 100-800 g.

It cross-breeds with the Bream, the White Bream, the Alburn and especially with the Roach. Hybrids with the Roach (3) have the fins redder than the Roach, and yellow eyes like the Rudd.

The species *Scardinius graecus* (4) lives only in slow-flowing waters in southern Greece. It differs from the similar Rudd in its more slender body and larger scales.

Asp
Aspius aspius
Cyprinidae

The Asp is distributed throughout central Europe east of the Elbe in rivers feeding the North, Baltic, Black and Caspian Seas, being absent from northern Scandinavia, France and England.

It inhabits the lowland reaches of larger rivers, dams, and rarely even the still waters of pools and old river arms. It seeks out places with a large area of open surface over deeper water with a gentle current and plenty of hiding places, to which it flees immediately when disturbed. It is a predatory fish with well-developed sight, being able to observe danger even on the bank. The Asp is at the same time a shy and usually a solitary fish, defending a territory in which it hunts food. When adult it lives mainly on fish, hunting by darting into shoals near the surface. This swift attack is often accompanied by splashing on the surface or even by jumping out of the water. It also gathers insects that have dropped on to the surface. It has an annual growth rate, depending on food conditions, of 0.5-1 kg, commonly growing to a weight of 6-8 kg and a length of 60-80 cm, and living for up to 15 years. Fish take part in their first spawning when 4-5 years old. The spawning takes place from April to June in the current above a gravelly or stony bed, the eggs adhering to the bottom. The fry hatch after 10-17 days. They live on zooplankton, smaller fish living on fry and insects, larger fish making the transition to the predatory feeding method.

It is exploited economically mainly in the former USSR, where it is fished with nets and fish-pots, for example in the Volga. It is a popular fish with anglers on account of its combative character, and has white, tough, tasty meat.

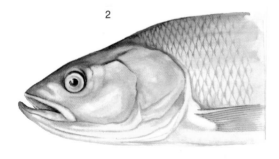

2

The Asp (1) is a large, slender fish, the shape of its body being reminiscent of a torpedo. It has a large terminal mouth, pointed pectoral fins and a deeply indented caudal fin. The belly is roundish in the front part, forming a keel covered with scales behind the ventral fins. It is the only predatory fish of the family Cyprinidae. It has a large mouth (2), the corners of which extend to below the eyes. The lower jaw is

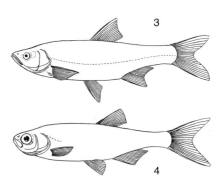

longer than the upper one and rises on its front edge into a hook-like protuberance. The jaws are strong and toothless and are used merely to seize hold of the prey. This is then swallowed whole, being crushed by teeth situated on the gullet bones in the oesophagus.

A young Asp (3) resembles the Moderlieschen (4), differing only in the larger mouth, smaller eyes and full lateral line.

107

Grass Carp
Ctenopharyngodon idella

Cyprinidae

The original habitat of the Grass Carp lies in the central and lower reaches of the river Amur and its tributaries, as well as rivers in China as far as the province of Canton and Taiwan. From there, the Grass Carp was in the course of time introduced into Europe, recently also into England and the USA. The Grass Carp is a fish predominantly of great, warm rivers with gentle flow, sufficient depth and an abundance of blind river arms and quiet backwaters with rich plant growth.

In its natural habitat it spawns from April to the end of summer, as soon as the water temperature rises to 15-18 °C. The fry hatch after approximately 2 days, and in the wild keep to the shallows near the bank, where they feed on minute zooplankton, changing over to plant food as soon as they reach the size of 3 cm. In Europe the Grass Carp does not reproduce naturally. It must be spawned artificially and the eggs incubated at a temperature of 25 °C. In artificial spawning, 50,000-150,000 eggs are produced per 1 kg of female weight. Outside the spawning period, the Grass Carp keeps to backwaters and river arms, where it feeds on aquatic plants, benthos and insects flying near the surface. In winter the level of its activity drops and it withdraws to deeper places of the main river bed, where young and adult fish overwinter in separate shoals.

In China, the Grass Carp has been economically exploited for the last 2,000 years. The introduction of the Grass Carp into Europe has not brought the expected results. In colder conditions it grows more slowly, and in carp ponds becomes an omnivore, competing with carps. It has more potential in biological control, eliminating unwanted plant growth in purpose-built courses and water reservoirs.

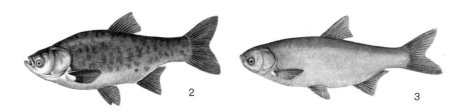

2

3

108

The Grass Carp (1) has an elongate, cylindrical body, the shape of which is reminiscent of the Chub, and its colouring reminiscent of the Carp. It has a striking broad forehead on its powerful head. The mouth is semi-ventral, and the gills rough, similar to those of the Crucian Carp. In its original habitat it attains a length of up to 120 cm and a weight of up to 32 kg. In European conditions, it usually attains a length of only 40-80 cm and a weight of 2-5 kg.

Two other herbivorous species — the Big Head Carp (*Aristichthys nobilis*) (2) and the Silver Carp (*Hypophthalmichthys molitrix*) (3) — have been introduced into Europe from the same region as the Grass Carp. The Silver Carp feeds exclusively on algae — phytoplankton — whereas in the case of *Aristichthys nobilis* algae form only half its diet, the other half consisting of minute fauna — zooplankton.

1

Moderlieschen, Belica
Leucaspius delineatus
Cyprinidae

The Moderlieschen is distributed throughout central and eastern Europe from the Rhine river-basin as far as the Volga basin, and in the region which feeds the Black Sea from the Danube as far as the Don. It is absent from England, the Iberian peninsula, Italy and France. It lives in pools, ponds, irrigation canals, blind river arms, lakes and other still waters with a rich growth of aquatic plant. It is an agile, gregarious fish, keeping in large shoals near the surface, where it feeds on phytoplankton and zooplankton.

Outside the spring season, it is not possible to distinguish the sexes in the Moderlieschen. The distinguishing characteristics appear in the period of sexual activity, that is from April to July. The female has a protruding three-part urogenital papilla, the male a depressed urogenital orifice, and a spawning rash on the head and body. The Moderlieschen is a thermophilic species which requires a minimum temperature of 18 °C for spawning. Therefore it spawns in Europe within a span of 4 months, depending on the geographical latitude of the spawning sites. The laying of the 100-2,300 eggs takes place in 3-5 batches. The eggs are very small and joined together in strings, the females hanging these on to aquatic plants, roots etc. The male guards the eggs for 10-12 days, until the fry disperse. The fry concentrate in large shoals, which feed on planktonic algae near the surface. The Moderlieschen is a short-lived fish, only exceptionally reaching an age of more than 3 years. It ranks among the smallest freshwater European fishes, growing to a length of only 7-9 cm, rarely up to 12 cm. In enclosed pools where there are no predatory fishes, it will over-reproduce and form 'dwarfish' populations attaining only 3 cm in length. It is of no economic importance but is from time to time used by anglers as bait.

3

The Moderlieschen (1) is a small slender fish with conspicuously large eyes and large scales which fall off easily. It is reminiscent in its body shape and dorsal mouth position of the Alburn, differing in its incomplete lateral line, which terminates just behind the gills. Sexual dimorphism manifests itself in the larger size of females.

Another small species of the family Cyprinidae is *Paraphoxinus adspersus* (2),

which attains a length of 8-9 cm, at most
10 cm. This occurs in some waters in
Dalmatia. Its body is covered with small
thin scales. This is a little researched
species.

  Paraphoxinus alepidotus (3) resembles
P. adspersus both in its body shape and
size. It has almost scaleless skin, only
a few scales growing along the lateral
line. It lives in some rivers in Dalmatia.
From the economic viewpoint, these
species are insignificant.

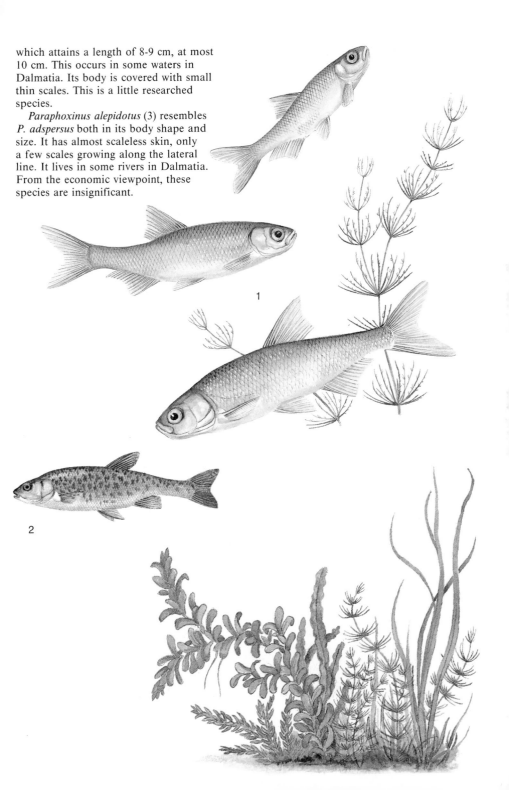

1

2

Tench
Tinca tinca
Cyprinidae

The Tench is distributed throughout the whole of Europe with the exception of northern Scandinavia, the northern part of Scotland, the Crimea and the western part of the Balkan peninsula. It can withstand even the mildly salt water of the eastern Baltic. It prefers still or gently flowing waters with a muddy bottom and rich aquatic plant growth in the lower courses of rivers, in pools, blind river arms, ponds and valley reservoirs. It displays great resistance to a shortage of oxygen and will even withstand acid peat waters. It is an undemanding and adaptable species. It seeks food among plant growth, its diet most frequently consisting of insect larvae, molluscs, worms and other small fauna. It also lives on bottom fauna, digging animals out of the mud with its snout and picking them out together with detritus using its protrusible ventral mouth. It grows relatively quickly, the female somewhat faster then the male, usually growing to a length of 30-40 cm and a weight of 1-2 kg, in exceptional cases up to 60 cm and 7 kg.

The Tench is a gregarious fish living in small shoals. Being a thermophilic species, it spawns relatively late from May to July. The 80,000-827,000 eggs are laid in 2-3 batches with intervals of up to fourteen days between. If the water temperature drops below 5 °C the Tench shoal withdraw to deep places, waiting out the winter motionless and without food just above the bottom or buried in mud.

The Tench is one of the best know fish species, being of considerable economic importance. Together with the Carp, it is kept as a supplementary species in ponds and dams in a number of European countries.

3

The Tench (1) has a short stout body with a conical head. Its colouring changes according to its surroundings: in shallow waters with sparse plant growth it is olive golden with yellowish-orange lips, in deeper water with rich growth it is darker olive green. The Tench is one of the few fishes in which it is possible to tell the sexes apart even outside the spawning period, according to the size and structure of the ventral fins (2). In adulthood these fins are pronounced large and longer

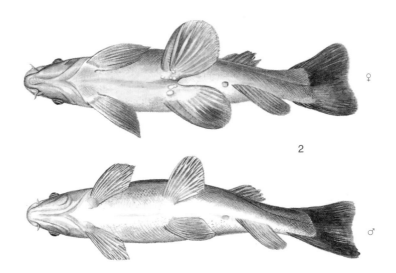

2

♀

♂

in males than in females, extending as far as the anal orifice or even beyond when laid against the body. Additionally a spawning rash appears in males during the spawning period.

In park reservoirs, garden ponds and aquaria, ornamental coloured forms of the Tench (3) — golden, red and also orange-coloured Tench with dark spots on the back are often kept.

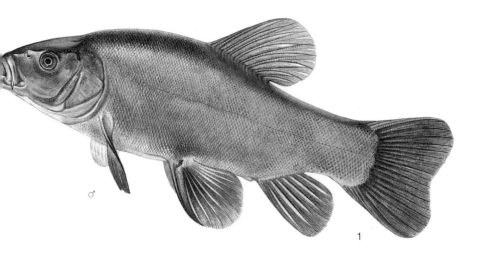

♂

1

Nase
Chondrostoma nasus
Cyprinidae

The Nase is absent in Europe from the north of the European part of Russia, from Scandinavia, Denmark, the British Isles and the Apennine peninsula. Until recently it was also absent from the Elbe river-basin, although penetrating its lower course through canals and water-passages from the Rhine. It inhabits swift-flowing barbel, grayling and sometimes trout zones, as well as adapting to life in the still waters of some dams. An essential condition for its occurrence is a stony bed with a rich growth of bacillaria and algae, which it eats all the year round together with small fauna.

In early spring when the temperature rises to 6-8 °C, shoals of Nase at least 3-4 years old migrate from the home reaches of rivers upstream to shallow sections with rapids to spawn. The shoals comprise up to several hundred individuals. The males, covered with a spawning rash, concentrate in the centre of the spawning site. The females gather under them in the current, swimming individually in among the males. These immediately surround the female, which spawns vigorously with several males at once, laying 800-1,000 eggs. In larger spawning grounds the bed is usually covered with a layer of eggs several centimetres deep after spawning is finished. Considerable losses are caused by mould and by predatory fishes which eat them. They develop for about 10 days at a temperature of 25 °C. The Nase is a moderately long-lived species, living up to 6-10 years.

Its meat is not particularly tasty, moreover containing a large number of muscle bones, but despite this it is fished for, mainly in the Rhine, the Danube, the Dnieper and the Volga.

The Nase (1) has an elongated, slender body, adapted to movement in swift water. The scales are large and the caudal fin deeply indented. The shape of the body is reminiscent of the related

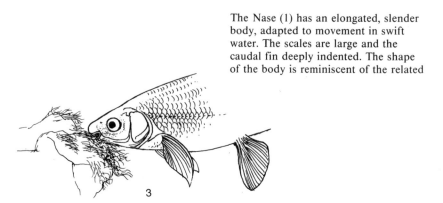

3

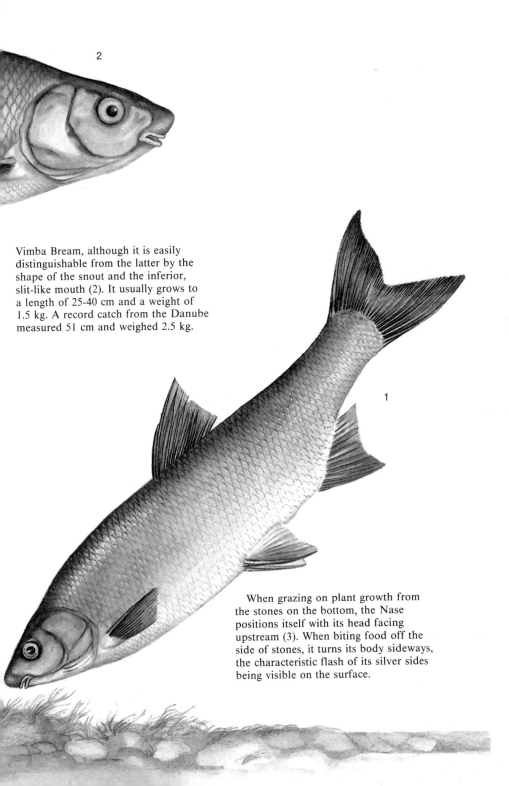

2

Vimba Bream, although it is easily distinguishable from the latter by the shape of the snout and the inferior, slit-like mouth (2). It usually grows to a length of 25-40 cm and a weight of 1.5 kg. A record catch from the Danube measured 51 cm and weighed 2.5 kg.

1

When grazing on plant growth from the stones on the bottom, the Nase positions itself with its head facing upstream (3). When biting food off the side of stones, it turns its body sideways, the characteristic flash of its silver sides being visible on the surface.

Toxostome, French Nase
Chondrostoma toxostoma

Cyprinidae

Apart from the Nase, a further species of *Chondrostoma* also lives in European waters.

The Toxostome lives in the rivers of south-west France, Spain and Portugal, in France sometimes living together with the Nase. It prefers small rivers and larger brooks with clean swift water and shallow stony reaches. It forms shoals of large numbers which withdraw to spawn, spawning from March to May on a gravelly bed, often even in small brooks. The female lays 500-8,000 eggs. The Toxostome lives mainly on algae, although to some extent also on small fauna living in the growth on stones. Its meat has little taste and is fatty with an abundance of small bones. Within its range its main significance is as a component of the diet of trout.

The Laska Nase (*Chondrostoma genei*) inhabits the central reaches of large rivers in central and northern Italy. Its mode of life does not differ substantially from that of the Nase. It is too rare a species to be of any practical importance. The Dalmatian Nase (*Chondrostoma kneri*) can only be found in the central reaches of rivers in Dalmatia and Bosnia. In view of the small area of its distribution and its low numbers it is of no economic importance. Another species known from former northern Yugoslavia is the Minnow Nase (*Chondrostoma phoxinus*), which inhabits shallows in swift-flowing upper reaches. Like other related species, it eats small bottom fauna, to a lesser extent also plants. Being a small, rare species it is of no economic significance.

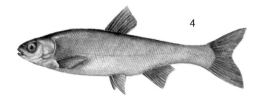

4

In its body shape, the Toxostome (1) resembles the Nase, although having a smaller snout and a small, arched mouth. It also attains a smaller size, 20-25 cm, rarely 30 cm, and a weight of 300-500 g.

116

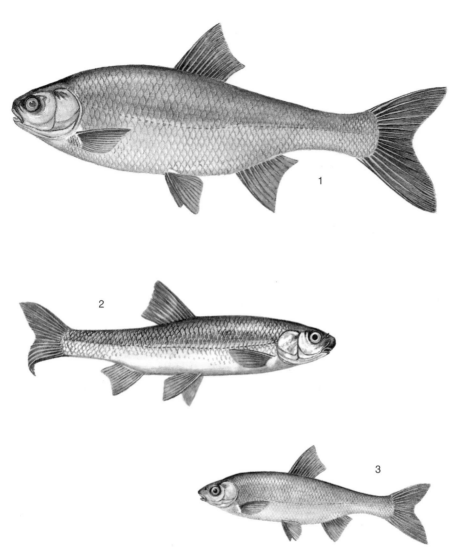

The Laska Nase (2) has the snout only
slightly developed, an arched mouth and
a striking dark stripe along its sides. It
grows to a length of only 15-20 cm, in
isolated cases up to 30 cm. The
Dalmatian Nase (3) resembles the Laska
Nase in the formation of the snout and
the arched mouth. At first glance,
however, it differs from the latter in the
absence of the dark stripe on the sides.
It grows to a length of only 15-18 cm,
20 cm at most. The Minnow Nase (4) is
the smallest of all the species
mentioned, growing to a length of 15 cm
only in isolated cases. It has the smallest
scales in comparison with other nases.
The biology of its reproduction is
unknown.

117

Gudgeon
Gobio gobio

Cyprinidae

The Gudgeon inhabits European waters except northern Scandinavia, Scotland, the Pyrenean peninsula, southern Italy and Greece, occurring as a whole range of subspecies within this extensive area. It lives in widely varied biotopes, ranging from mountain brooks to pools, valley reservoirs, ponds and lowland river reaches. It even occurs in sea water with a lower salt concentration in the northern and eastern Baltic. It requires clear, warmish water with a gentle current and a stony or sandy bottom. It spawns from April to June. The female lays 800-3,000 eggs stuck together in small clusters in 3-4 batches at intervals of several days. The fry hatch after 6-20 days, keeping together in the vicinity of the spawning site, where they hunt minute food, mainly zooplankton, at the bottom. Adult Gudgeon are highly voracious. Their feeding activity does not decrease even in winter, when they move to deeper places. The Gudgeon matures in its 2-3rd year, usually living up to 3 years. It is of no great economic significance. In some countries, for example in France, it is fished for preparation of typical national dishes. It serves as food for predatory fishes.

Kessler's Gudgeon (*Gobio kessleri*) is similar to the Gudgeon. It occurs in the river-basins of the Danube and the Dniestr, in Romania in the rivers Vilsan and Arges, in the area feeding the Baltic and in Poland in the river San. It lives in submontane rivers and brooks, in shallow reaches with rapids and a strong current. It attains a length of only 10-12 cm, rarely up to 15 cm. There is no detailed knowledge of its life.

The Gudgeon (1) has an elongated, spindle-shaped body, almost circular in cross-section with a slightly flattened belly. It is reminiscent of the Barbel, both in its body shape and in the short barbels at the mouth, which has an ventral position. Unlike the Barbel, however, it has only one pair of fleshy barbels at the corners of the mouth, extending at most to the level of the hind edge of the eye. The Gudgeon is a small fish attaining 10-15 cm in length and weighing 100-200 g.

118

1

When disturbed, it can find a depression in the bed and press itself against it at lightning speed, becoming motionless. The protective, spotted colouring corresponds in its shade to the environment in which the fish lives (2). Fish from deeper waters, where the bottom is of a monotonous colour, are darker and the spotting is less contrasting, fish from clear shallow waters with a gravelly bottom being lighter, with more pronounced spots.

Kessler's Gudgeon (3) is striking for the dark stripe along its lateral line.

2

119

Whitefin Gudgeon
Gobio albipinnatus

Cyprinidae

The Whitefin Gudgeon is distributed in the river-basins of the Danube, the Dnieper, the Don and Volga. Unlike the Gudgeon, it tends to occur more in the central and lower reaches of lowland rivers, although it does not avoid places with still water and mud deposits. In bankside pools in flood zones after a drop in the water level, large shoals of Whitefin Gudgeon fry appear.

The Whitefin Gudgeon is a gregarious fish. In the deeper parts of rivers it gathers in shoals, in which there are also fish of other species but of the same size. One of its companions in these shoals is often the Gudgeon. The shoals comb the bottom hunting small fauna, mainly worms, crustaceans and insect larvae. The Whitefin Gudgeon is a smaller species than its relatives, attaining a length of only 8-12 cm, rarely 13 cm. It spawns in the spring months. During this period, the males can be distinguished by their spawning rash. Detailed knowledge about its life is still lacking.

In places where it occurs in larger numbers it is an important food for predatory species. It is utilised locally as bait by anglers.

The Whitefin Gudgeon (1) resembles the Gudgeon and the Danube Gudgeon (*Gobio uranoscopus*) in its body shape and colouring, differing from them in its uniformly pale dorsal and caudal fins.

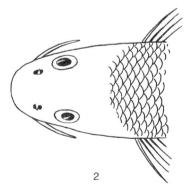

2

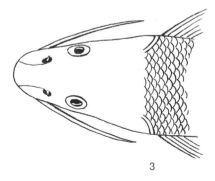

3

120

1

The Whitefin Gudgeon (2) furthermore differs from the Danube Gudgeon (3) in its shorter barbels and in the scaling on the upper part of the head, which in the case of the Whitefin Gudgeon extends further towards the snout. Differences can also be found on the throat, which in the Whitefin Gudgeon (4) is unscaled and in the Danube Gudgeon scaled (5).

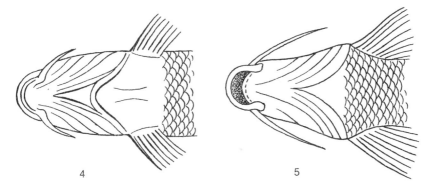

4   5

Danube Gudgeon
Gobio uranoscopus

Cyprinidae

The Danube Gudgeon occurs only in central Europe, in the Danube basin. It inhabits rapids in both small and large submontane rivers, giving preference to reaches with a strong current, terraces and wild water. In suitable places it forms small groups which keep to the bottom at a depth of 25-50 cm. It spawns in May and June in the current among stones overgrown with vegetation. As is the case with other species in this family, its diet consists of bottom fauna, in which insect larvae, worms and crustaceans prevail. Danube Gudgeon numbers are low and it is a rare species. As a result of the pollution of rivers and physical interference with their flow, its numbers are constantly declining. It has therefore been included among the protected species in many countries.

The Caucasian Gudgeon (*Gobio ciscaucasicus*) is distributed in the south-west part of the former USSR in the river-basins of the Terek, the Kuban, the Kuma, the Sulak and other rivers. It reproduces from May to June, greater detail about its spawning habits not being known. Like other gobies, it eats bottom fauna. It attains a length of 11-14 cm, rarely 15 cm.

A true intermediary stage between the gobies and barbels is represented by the Dalmatian Barbelgudgeon (*Aulopyge hugeli*). It occurs only in Dalmatia and Bosnia. It lives at the bottom in swift-flowing waters, where it seeks out small animals, mainly insect larvae and worms. In spite of attaining a maximum length of only 13 cm, it is of local economic importance.

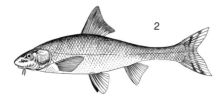

2

The Danube Gudgeon (1) is the only European species to have a scaled throat. The typical, long fleshy barbels extend behind the eyes as far as the gills. 5-6 dark spots which continue over the back to the sides fulfil the function of protective colouring when viewed from above. Thanks to this and its size, it is able to escape attention.

1

The Caucasian Gudgeon (2) resembles barbels. It has a somewhat higher body, which is of an inconspicuous olive greenish colour and without spots. The throat is unscaled in most individuals, but fish with fully scaled throats do occur. The barbels are relatively long, extending behind the level of the hind edge of eye. The Dalmatian Barbelgudgeon (3) has a long snout with 4 barbels, an elongated lower jaw, an undulating lateral line and smooth unscaled skin. Females differ from males in their broader bodies.

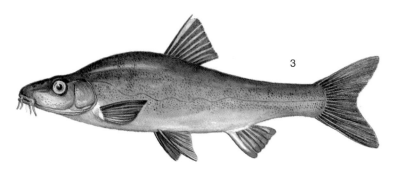

3

Barbel
Barbus barbus
Cyprinidae

The Barbel is distributed throughout western and central Europe, including the Danube basin. It is absent from Scandinavia, Denmark, Ireland and the peninsulas of southern Europe. It can be found in the mainstream of a river on a gravelly bottom with sufficient stones, among which it seeks refuge. It is a typical fish for the deeper, swift-flowing reaches of upper and central river courses, which have been named after it — the barbel zone.

It is active mainly at night, but will feed in the daytime after a storm, when the rush of water brings small animals washed down by the rain. The main source of food, however, is found on the river bottom. Barbel search through the sand and gravel of the bottom in groups of variable size, grouping the stones with their barbels, and then turning them over using the snout so they can reach the worms, molluscs and insect larvae hidden underneath them. The Barbel further enriches its diet with eggs, fry and from time to time also with small fishes, not avoiding even plant food. When the water cools down, it stops taking food and survives the winter in a state of rest in deeper places of the river. From the ecological viewpoint its value lies mainly in the fact that it seeks out its food in the main riverbed where there is a relatively strong current, whereas other species living in the same environment keep more to the banks.

In the period from May to August, Barbel shoals migrate to higher reaches to spawn. The females lay up to 50,000 eggs. A spawning rash appears in males. Females grow faster than males and attain a larger size. The Barbel is a favourite angling fish. The ideal time to fish for it is towards evening or in muddy water after rain.

3

The Barbel (1) is a robust, cylindrical fish with a flat belly. Its body is covered with small scales. The colouring is adapted to the colour of the bottom in deeper water. Younger individuals, which keep to shallows, have irregular spots on the body. It usually attains a length of 30-60 cm, 0.5-2 kg in weight, rarely up to 1 m and 8-12 kg. A record catch from the Dnieper weighed 16 kg.

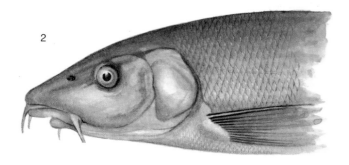

2

4   5

The Barbel has a high but short dorsal fin (4). The last hard ray of this is markedly toothed. In the related Southern Barbel (*Barbus meridionalis*), this ray is smooth (5).

The Barbel mouth (2) has a ventral position and is bordered with fleshy lips and four barbels. The ventral position of the mouth and the location of the barbels can be seen when viewed from below (3).

1

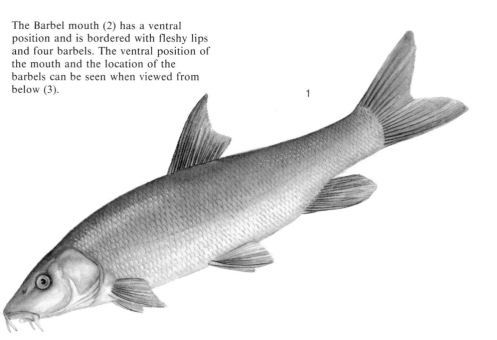

Southern Barbel
Barbus meridionalis

Cyprinidae

The Southern Barbel occurs in distinct and separate populations in the south-western part of the Pyrenean peninsula, southern France, northern Italy, the Balkans and in the northern part of the Carpathian arc in the Wisla, the Danube, and the Dnieper. It inhabits an environment similar to that of the Barbel, but prefers the higher reaches of courses — the grayling zone. In places where both species live together, cross-breeding occurs. From May to June Southern Barbel shoals go further upstream to the spawning sites. They spawn in the current over a gravelly and stony bottom, sometimes also in aquatic plant growth. The males are conspicuous with their spawning rash. The hatched fry seek out shallow backwaters with still water, where they gather in shoals and hunt minute plankton.

In their territories, adult individuals keep among stones in the mainstream, or in the vicinity of underwashed banks, where they can find both food and shelter. Their diet consists of small bottom fauna. Unlike the Barbel, the Southern Barbel stays in its original territory even in winter. On account of its smaller size, it is of lesser economic significance than the Barbel, rather serving as food for predatory fishes, mainly Salmonidae.

Within its distribution it occurs as a whole range of subspecies. In addition, the Turkish Barbel (*Barbus cyclolepis*) lives in flowing water in the river-basins of some rivers feeding the Baltic, Black and Aegean Seas, for example in the rivers Wisla, Struma, or Maritsa. It is of no economic significance.

The Southern Barbel (1) is smaller than the Barbel. It grows to a length of 20-30 cm and a weight of 150-250 g, only rarely up to 40 cm and 500 g. On its back, sides and fins, it has irregular spots, not only when young but also in adulthood. The scales are larger than in the Barbel.

The Southern Barbel (2) differs from the Barbel (3) in its longer anal fin, which when folded extends at least as far as the base of the caudal fin. The last hard ray of the dorsal fin is smooth (4), whereas in the Barbel it is toothed (5).

126

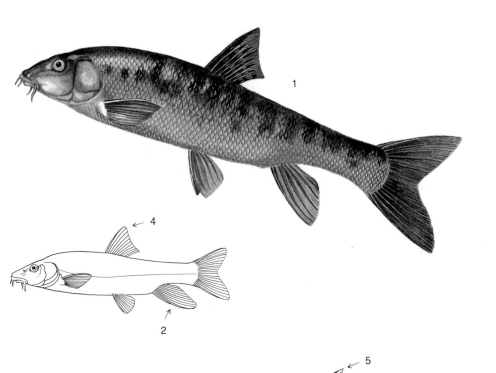

1

← 4

2

← 5

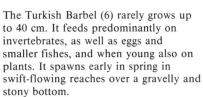

3

The Turkish Barbel (6) rarely grows up to 40 cm. It feeds predominantly on invertebrates, as well as eggs and smaller fishes, and when young also on plants. It spawns early in spring in swift-flowing reaches over a gravelly and stony bottom.

6

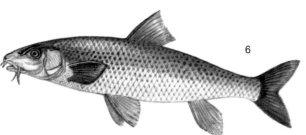

Caspian Barbel
Barbus brachycephalus Cyprinidae

The Caspian Barbel occurs in the salt water of the south-west part of the Caspian Sea and in the Aral Sea. It ascends to the upper reaches of rivers to spawn. The main migration takes place in June and July. Females become sexually mature during migration and during their stay in the river. They do not spawn, however, until April to May of the following year. The fecundity of females is relatively high, ranging from 1,000,000-1,500,000 eggs. The hatched fry are carried downstream to the lower reaches of rivers. Of the young fish, the females mostly return to the sea straight away, whilst the males usually remain in fresh waters for 3-5 years. After they mature sexually and spawn for the first time they generally return to the sea. In the sea, Caspian Barbel feed mainly on marine molluscs, and during the stay in rivers on freshwater molluscs and other bottom fauna, including smaller fishes. During their migration to rivers, they do not feed at all. The Caspian Barbel is an economically important species, being caught mainly in the period of spawning migration.

The species *Barbus plebejus* inhabits the southern Alps, the whole of Italy, Sicily, and Dalmatia. Like other barbel species, it lives in clear, swiftly flowing water with a hard bottom. It eats bottom fauna and plant fragments. It is of local economic significance.

In the upper and central reaches of rivers flowing into the Caspian Sea lives the Caucasian Barbel (*Barbus ciscaucasicus*). The Greek Barbel (*Barbus graecus*) is known to live only in the river Aspropotamus in Greece. It is a medium-sized fish of local economic importance.

The Caspian Barbel (1) is a large fish, attaining a size of 0.5-1 m and weighing 2-6 kg. A record catch measured 120 cm and weighed 25 kg. In relation to its body, this Barbel has smaller scales than other species. In the Amur delta, individuals occur in isolated cases with greatly elongated bodies (the *panachan* form). The cause of the origin of this form is unknown.

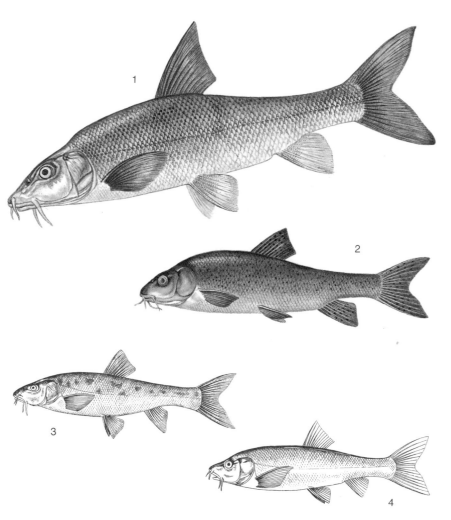

The characteristic features of *Barbus plebejus* (2) are small irregular spots on the body and on unpaired fins. It attains a length of only 25-30 cm. The Caucasian Barbel (3) has greenish colouring with darker spots and a yellowish belly. It grows up to 20-35 cm in length, rarely up to 39 cm. The Greek Barbel (4) has brownish-yellow colouring, the back being brownish and the belly yellowish. It attains 30-40 cm in length, in isolated cases up to 45 cm.

129

Bleak
Alburnus alburnus

Cyprinidae

The Bleak lives throughout almost the whole of Europe, being absent only from northern Scandinavia, Scotland, Ireland and southern peninsulas. It occurs in large numbers in places with slowly-flowing or still water in the lower and central reaches of rivers. It can commonly be encountered in valley reservoirs, lakes in abandoned gravel quarries and in pools in flood zones. It shoals near the surface, where it gathers animals which have dropped on to the surface. It will jump out of the water for an insect flying near the surface, in the water hunting insect larvae and zooplankton. In winter it reduces its intake of food and withdraws to deeper places. In waters without predators it is able greatly to over-reproduce. It spawns from the end of April to the beginning of July. Shoals of sexually mature (at least 1-3 year-old) fish seek out still bankside waters without any current. The males in the shoals are conspicuous with their spawning rash. The females stick the 5,000-6,500 eggs on to plants, as well as on to clean gravelly substrate. Within a single year, the young fish will grow up to 10 cm, which is half the length they will attain in their whole life, which seldom exceeds 6 years. The Bleak represents an important dietary component for predatory fishes. In some dams it is caught with nets and sometimes it is even caught by anglers.

The Riffle Minnow, or Schneider (*Alburnoides bipunctatus*), has a similar distribution to that of the previous species, except that it does not extend as far north or south. It mostly inhabits reaches with shallow clear water. The biology of the two species does not differ substantially. The Riffle Minnow has smaller eggs, their number therefore being higher.

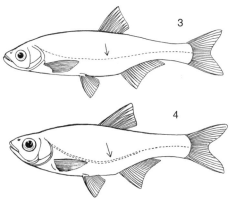

The Bleak (1) has a slender, flat-sided body with an almost straight back. The head is small, with large eyes and a terminal mouth pointing upwards. The body is covered with relatively large scales which come off easily. Between the ventral fins and the anus there is a sharp scaleless keel. In lakes and dam reservoirs it occurs in high-bodied, archbacked forms. It attains a length of 15-17 cm, at a weight of 15-30 g. The largest caught fish measured 25 cm and weighed 111 g.

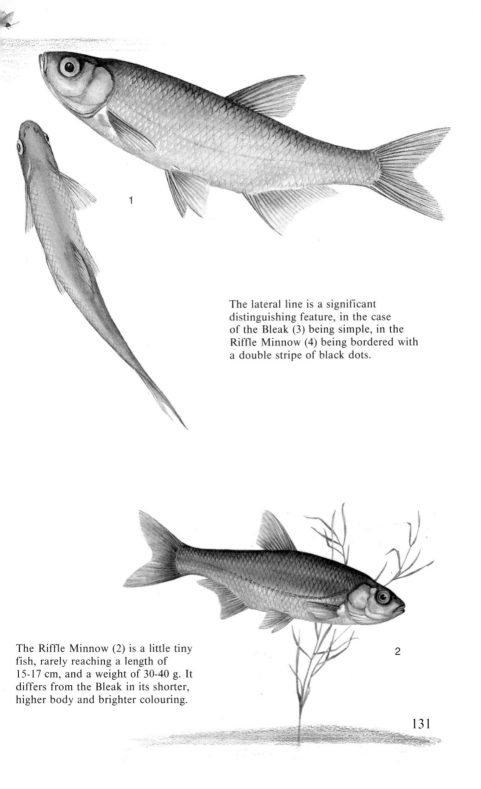

The lateral line is a significant
distinguishing feature, in the case
of the Bleak (3) being simple, in the
Riffle Minnow (4) being bordered with
a double stripe of black dots.

1

2

The Riffle Minnow (2) is a little tiny
fish, rarely reaching a length of
15-17 cm, and a weight of 30-40 g. It
differs from the Bleak in its shorter,
higher body and brighter colouring.

131

Danube Bleak
Chalcalburnus chalcoides

This species is distributed in the rivers feeding the Black and Caspian Seas and the Sea of Azov, and in the brackish water of these seas. It also lives in the Aral Sea. It occurs in permanent and migratory forms. The permanent freshwater form inhabits the tributaries of the upper course of the Danube, Alpine lakes and the brackish water of the Aral Sea. Migratory forms inhabit the brackish waters of the coastal parts of seas.

Fish 3-7 years old migrate to rivers to spawn. Migration occurs during autumn and winter when the fish ascend to central reaches and overwinter. In spring they continue their journey and in May and June they spawn. In some rivers the fish migrate early in spring and begin to spawn immediately after arriving at the spawning site. Males can be distinguished by the spawning rash on the head and front part of the body. The spawning itself takes place at night, the females laying 2,500-40,000 eggs. The fry hatch after 2-3 days, and after digesting the yolk-sac drift slowly downstream to the sea. Adult fish return to the sea as quickly as possible. Not having taken any food during migration, they feed intensively on the return journey. They feed on bottom fauna, plankton, insect larvae, surface insects, fry and small fishes.

The Danube Bleak is very numerous in some parts of its distribution. As it attains a considerable size and the meat of the migratory forms is fatty and very tasty, it is of great economic importance. It is fished for during migration in barraged rivers. The resident forms are caught less frequently as they grow more slowly and their meat is not of such high quality.

The Danube Bleak (1) is a slender, long fish. The position of the anal fin is shifted towards the back, so that its base is behind that of the dorsal fin. It has the typical colouring of open water fishes. The dark back protects the fish when viewed from above, and the light belly renders it invisible when seen from below. It grows to a length of up to 40 cm and a weight of 800 g.

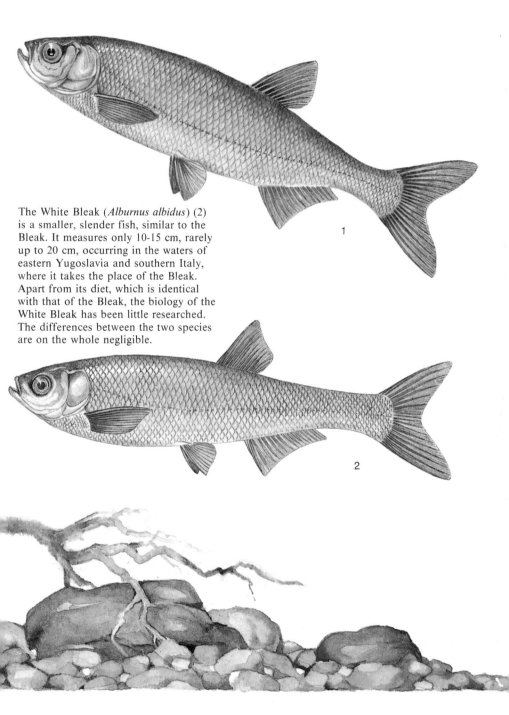

The White Bleak (*Alburnus albidus*) (2) is a smaller, slender fish, similar to the Bleak. It measures only 10-15 cm, rarely up to 20 cm, occurring in the waters of eastern Yugoslavia and southern Italy, where it takes the place of the Bleak. Apart from its diet, which is identical with that of the Bleak, the biology of the White Bleak has been little researched. The differences between the two species are on the whole negligible.

1

2

133

Silver Bream, White Bream
Blicca bjoerkna

Cyprinidae

The Silver Bream is distributed in European waters from France as far as the Urals, being absent from southern peninsulas and the north of Norway, Sweden, Finland and the British Isles. It inhabits the lower reaches of larger rivers in the bream zone, valley reservoirs, lakes, blind river arms and pools. It seeks quiet places, where it keeps to the bottom in deeper waters. In some waters it is very abundant. Where predatory fishes are rare, it over-reproduces and forms stunted populations. From April to June it swims into bankside shallows to spawn. At the northern margin of its area of distribution, the spawning period is extended until July. Males have a spawning rash on the body and on the first rays of the pectoral fins. Females lay 11,000-109,000 eggs on to aquatic plants and other submerged objects, including stones on the bottom. They do not lay all the eggs at once, but in 2-3 batches. The eggs from the first batch are the largest. Its spawning sites, as well as the period of spawning, are often shared by the Bream, Roach and Rudd. Hybrids between these species do occur, but are infertile. Silver Bream fry hatch after 10-14 days. After digesting the yolk-sac supply, they feed on zooplankton, more mature fishes on insect larvae and plant fragments. The males become partially mature as early as in the 2nd year, females in the 3rd-5th year. The Silver Bream can live for up to 16 years.

Despite being an abundant species, the Silver Bream is of little importance, as its meat is of poor quality, with a great number of intermuscular bones. From the ecological viewpoint, it forms an important component in the diet of predatory fishes.

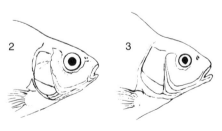

The Silver Bream (1) has a high, laterally flattened body, a relatively small head, large eyes and a small semi-ventral mouth. In adult fish, there is a stripe of unscaled skin behind the head on the front part of the back. The keel between the ventral and anal fins is also scaleless. The fish attains a length of 15-20 cm, in isolated cases 35 cm, and a weight of 500 g. Record catches weighed 1.2-1.8 kg.

At first sight, the Silver Bream resembles the Common Bream, differing

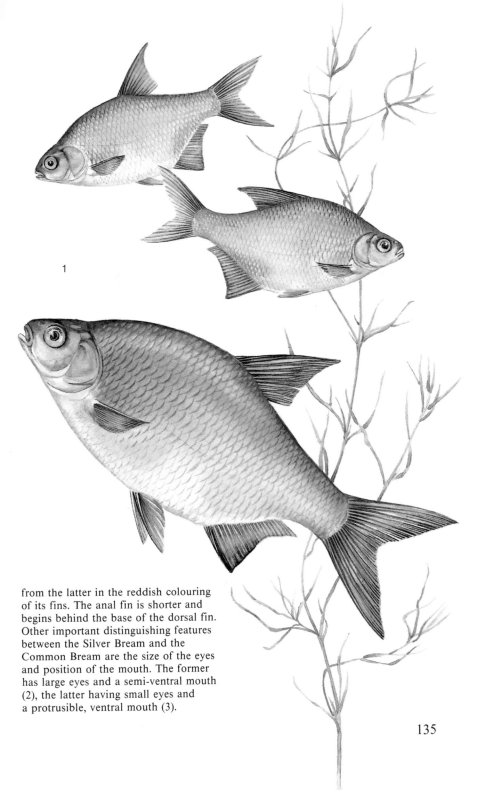

1

from the latter in the reddish colouring of its fins. The anal fin is shorter and begins behind the base of the dorsal fin. Other important distinguishing features between the Silver Bream and the Common Bream are the size of the eyes and position of the mouth. The former has large eyes and a semi-ventral mouth (2), the latter having small eyes and a protrusible, ventral mouth (3).

Common Bream
Abramis brama

Cyprinidae

The Common Bream is distributed throughout almost the whole of Europe, with the exception of northern Scandinavia, Scotland, the Pyrenean and Apennine peninsulas, and the western and southern parts of the Balkan peninsula.

It is a typical fish for the lower reaches of larger rivers, known as the bream zone. It also occurs in valley reservoirs, blind river arms, pools, ponds and lakes left behind in abandoned gravel quarries. It will even tolerate brackish water in the estuaries of some rivers. It keeps to deeper, open water, swimming to the bank at night or early in the evening in search of food, or in April to June for spawning. The females lay up to 587,000 eggs in 1-3 batches on aquatic plants, roots, or on a substitute substrate, for example gravel on the bottom of newly-built dams, or even on banks made of dumped quarried sharp-edged gravel. As spawning is collective and vigorous, injuries and the consequent death of large numbers of fish can occur when spawning on an unsuitable substrate. In order to protect the Common Bream, fishermen place artificial nests made of bound twigs, most frequently spruce, into waters without plant growth. At a temperature of 12-16 °C, the eggs develop and hatch in 3-4 days.

The Common Bream ranks among the large fish species. In common with other species, growth of an individual depends on the abundance of the population, as well as on the abundance of other fish species competing for food. In case of a shortage of food or lack of predatory fishes, it forms slow-growing, stunted populations. It is an economically significant fish species. In central Europe in particular, it is used in fish farms and has tasty, relatively fatty meat.

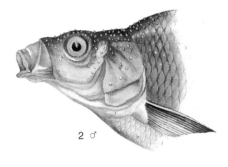

2 ♂

The Common Bream (1) has a strikingly high, flat-sided body, covered with large scales which fall off easily. The head is relatively small in comparison with the body. The fins are long, pointed, and greyish-blue in colour. The sharp scaleless keel extends to the anal orifice between the ventral fins and the anal fin is long. The Common Bream usually attains a length of 30-40 cm, weighing 0.5-2 kg. Common Bream populations do not mature within a narrow age span

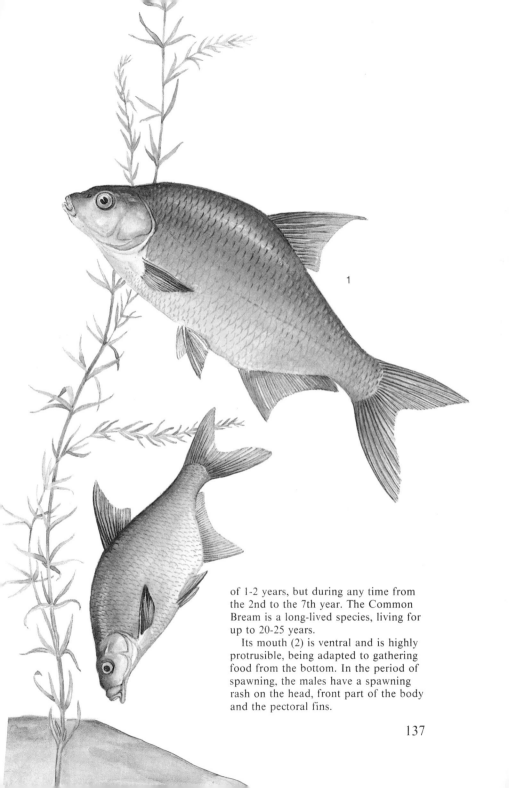

of 1-2 years, but during any time from the 2nd to the 7th year. The Common Bream is a long-lived species, living for up to 20-25 years.

Its mouth (2) is ventral and is highly protrusible, being adapted to gathering food from the bottom. In the period of spawning, the males have a spawning rash on the head, front part of the body and the pectoral fins.

Danube Bream, Whiteye Bream
Abramis sapa   Cyprinidae

The Danube Bream lives in larger rivers feeding the Baltic, Black and Caspian Seas and the Sea of Azov and in the region feeding the Aral Sea. Apart from the permanent freshwater form, migratory forms also occur in brackish waters, migrating to fresh river waters to spawn. Sexually mature, 3-4 year-old fish migrate in April and May upstream to shallower places. The female lays the 5,000-42,000 eggs in the stream over a gravelly bottom. After spawning, the parent fish return to their home reaches. Young fish feed on zooplankton, larger fish predominantly on bottom food, as well as on plant fragments and detritus. In comparison with other species, the Danube Bream grows slowly, and is the smallest and least numerous species of the Cyprinidae family.

The Zope or Blue Bream (*Abramis ballerus*) ranks among medium-sized species of the Cyprinidae family. It occurs in fresh waters feeding the North, Baltic, Black and Caspian Seas from the Rhine to the Neva and from the Danube to the Urals. It inhabits quiet waters in low river reaches, as well as the still waters of dams, pools or blind river arms. In many places in the bream zone, it is more abundant than the Common Bream. Sporadically it even swims into brackish waters. In April and May it migrates in shoals to shallows with current and aquatic plant cover to spawn. It matures in its 3-4th year and lives up to 18 years. It is an important commercial species. In large rivers, for example in the Danube and in some valley reservoirs, it forms a substantial proportion of catches when fished with nets.

The Danube Bream (1) has a relatively longer and lower body in comparison with other breams, although attaining the smallest size. Fish 10 years old measure about 25 cm, their weight being about 300 g.

The Zope (2), in comparison with the similar Common Bream, is smaller, more slender and has a more pointed head. The Zope lives in many places together with the Danube Bream, but in spite of this does not compete with it for food. The ventral position of the mouth of the Danube Bream (3) bears witness to the fact that it gathers food from the bottom. The terminal mouth of the Zope (4), on the other hand, which points upwards, is adapted to hunting planktonic food in the water column.

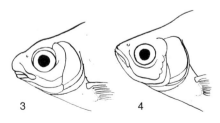

3   4

138

Both the Danube Bream and the Zope have a long anal fin (5) with 37-48 rays. The Common Bream and Silver Bream have a shorter anal fin (6), with only 21-30 rays.

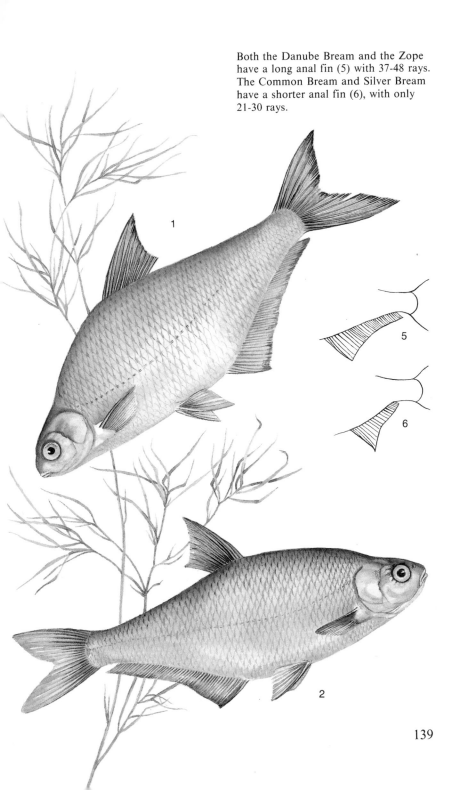

East European Bream, Vimba
Vimba vimba

Cyprinidae

The East European Bream is distributed in waters feeding the North and Baltic Seas from the Weser to the Neva, in southern Sweden and in Finland, as well as in the rivers feeding the Black and Caspian Seas from the Danube to the Urals. It lives in shoals in the bream zone in the lower reaches of rivers. As a semi-migratory species, it undergoes migrations up to several hundred kilometres long, penetrating as far as the barbel zone in the central reaches of rivers. It prefers deeper water over a stony and gravelly bottom, but can also be found in some valley reservoirs and lakes, and sometimes even in brackish water. For spawning, it migrates upstream in shoals. Fish 3-4 years old spawn from the end of April until July in more gentle currents over a stony bottom. The female usually lays up to 200,000 viscous eggs in 2-3 batches. Until they digest the yolk-sac, the larvae lie passively among the stones on the bottom. The fry live on zooplankton. Larger fish grub in the bottom with their snouts, and pick out insect larvae, worms, and other small invertebrates with their slightly protrusible mouths.

The hindering of the spawning migration caused by the construction of technical facilities, as well as the increasing pollution of rivers, have recently brought about a discernible drop in East European Bream numbers. The East European Bream has tasty meat, especially in the winter months, when its fat content increases. In some places it is of great economic significance. It is keenly fished for by anglers. Catches commonly attain lengths of 20-30 cm and a weight ,of 250-500 g, rarely 40-50 cm and 1-3 kg.

3 ♂

The East European Bream (1) superficially resembles breams, but differs from them, however, in its lower, more elongated body and the position of the dorsal fin, which begins at the perpendicular line from the rear end of the base of the ventral fins. From broad-snouts it differs by the dorsal fin and the shape of the mouth. Typical characteristics of the East European Bream are the shape of the head, the scaleless keel on the back between the head and the dorsal fin, and the scaled

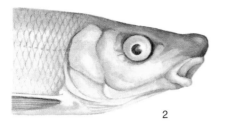

keel behind this fin. The head of this fish is elongated, terminating in a sharp snout (2), under which there is a ventral arched mouth with fleshy lips. It is one of the few cyprinid species which markedly change their colouring during the period of spawning. Males (3) are dark to black on the back and sides. This black colour contrasts sharply with the orange lower part of the head, belly and paired fins. A spawning rash appears on the head and back.

2

1

Ziege, Chekhon
Pelecus cultratus

Cyprinidae

The Ziege occurs in two forms within its range — the area feeding the Baltic Sea from the Oder to the Neva, the Black Sea from the Danube to the Kuban, the Caspian Sea and the Aral Sea. The semi-migratory form lives mainly in the semi-fresh water of the estuaries of large rivers. It migrates to the fresh water of rivers to spawn. Migration takes place in two periods, and is most numerous at the end of summer, from July until the rivers freeze. In spring, from April to May, a second migration period occurs in a few fish. The females lay the 10,000-58,000 eggs in sections of the main river bed with rapids, or in flooded shallows with a strong current. The eggs are pelagic and drift downstream, swelling in the water. At a temperature of 12 °C their development takes 3-4 days. The hatched larvae, like the eggs, continue to drift downstream. The fry live on zooplankton, larger fish on insects which have fallen on to the surface and from the second year onwards mostly on fishes. At first they hunt the fry of other fish species, and later smallish fish, mainly herring in brackish water. Apart from semi-migratory forms, the Ziege also occurs in resident forms living permanently in the main stream in the lower reaches of large rivers and in river arms with a through-flow of water. It is a surface fish, keeping in shoals close to the water surface, where it seeks food.

The Ziege is economically exploited in the regions of the Black and Caspian Seas, as well as of the Aral Sea. It has fatty meat with a great number of small bones which is not particularly tasty when fresh, therefore mostly being smoked. Recently, Ziege numbers have been steadily declining.

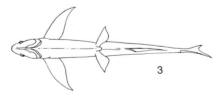

The Ziege (1) is more reminiscent in its body shape of the Herring or flying fishes than of a cyprinid species. A striking feature is its straight back with the short dorsal fin, which is positioned as far back as above the anal fin. Other special characteristics are the belly, which is curved into an arched shape, and the greatly undulating lateral line. The caudal fin is deeply indented.

142

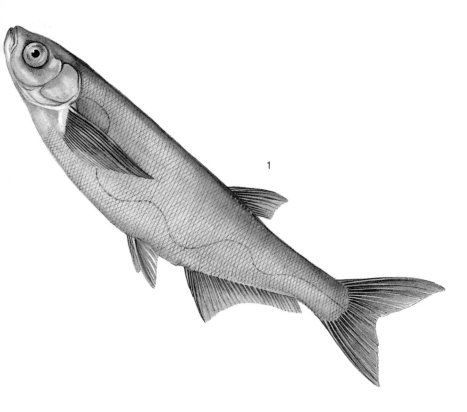

1

The body is covered with scales which fall off easily. The Ziege usually lives to an age of 8 years at a size of 30-40 cm and a weight of 300-400 g. Record catches involve semi-migratory populations.

On the head of the Ziege (2) there are large conspicuous eyes and a large, pronouncedly dorsal mouth. From a ventral view (3), the lateral compression of the body and the long, pointed pectoral fins are clearly visible. The sharp, scaleless keel forms the ridge of the belly, being drawn in the illustration as a lengthwise line.

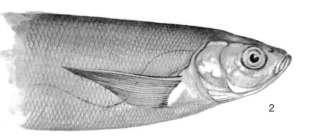

2

Bitterling
Rhodeus sericeus

The Bitterling is distributed to the north of the Alps, but is absent from Scandinavia, Denmark and most of the British Isles. The western margin of its main area of distribution is formed by the Rhône river basin, and the eastern by the Caspian Sea region.

It inhabits muddy backwaters in the lower reaches of rivers, old river arms, small overgrown lakes and pools. Swan Mussels (genus *Anodonta*) and freshwater clams (genus *Unio*) also share these habitats, and their presence is an absolute necessity for the successful reproduction of the Bitterling, which takes place from April to August. During this period, a 5-6 cm long ovipositor grows on the female behind the anal orifice. The males, which in spring have sought out 'their' mussel, at first drive other males away from it, as well as sexually immature females. If a sexually mature female approaches, however, they start to entice her towards the mussel by performing a complex ritual. A single female lays only 40-100 eggs into the gill chamber of the mussel. The male either entices other females to the same mussel, or leaves it to another pair. In one mussel there can be up to 200 eggs, which hide among the gill lamellae throughout the whole period of their development, that is 15-20 days. They do not leave the mussel until reaching the fry stage, 2-3 days after digesting the yolk-sac. Thereafter, they live predominantly on zoo- and phytoplankton, fully grown fish on bottom-dwelling animals. The Bitterling is a short-lived fish, living up to a maximum of five years. It attains a length of 5-8 cm, rarely even 10 cm. It is of no commercial importance. Its meat is bitter to our taste, but its natural predators do not mind. On account of its bright colouring and interesting biology, it is sometimes kept in aquaria.

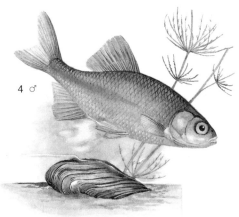

4 ♂

The Bitterling (1) is a small fish. It differs from the similar Crucian Carp in its shinier, brighter body, as well as in the absence of a dark spot at the base of the caudal fin, which is typical of young Crucian Carp. In the spawning period, males differ from females in their brighter colouring and in the spawning rash developing on their bodies.

The reproduction of the Bitterling is a relatively complex ritual. The male entices a female to a mussel. The female finds its excretory orifice (2) by means of the water current, inserting into it the

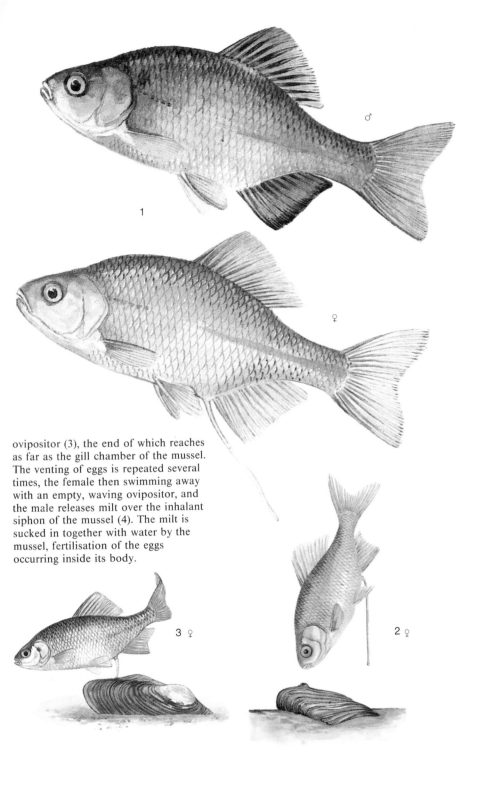

1

♂

♀

ovipositor (3), the end of which reaches
as far as the gill chamber of the mussel.
The venting of eggs is repeated several
times, the female then swimming away
with an empty, waving ovipositor, and
the male releases milt over the inhalant
siphon of the mussel (4). The milt is
sucked in together with water by the
mussel, fertilisation of the eggs
occurring inside its body.

3 ♀

2 ♀

Crucian Carp
Carassius carassius

Cyprinidae

The Crucian Carp was originally found in the rivers feeding the North, Baltic and Black Seas, as well as in those feeding the Arctic Ocean as far as the river Lena. However, it has been introduced along with the Wild Carp into other places in Europe. It inhabits mainly still, heavily overgrown, lowland waters with a muddy bottom, being relatively rare in rivers. Together with the Carp, it has been introduced into ponds, and recently even into some reservoirs. It is an undemanding, adaptable species which occurs in waters in which no other species would survive. For example it is even found in densely overgrown shallow ponds which almost freeze solid in winter and in summer heat up considerably, the oxygen content dropping to zero. Depending on environmental conditions, it occurs in a whole range of body shapes and sizes, from a high-bodied, quickly growing form to stunted populations. The characteristics of these are not hereditary: when stunted forms are transferred into better conditions, a change into the high-bodied form occurs in the next generation.

The typical Crucian Carp environment has aquatic growth on the bottom, where the fish seeks small fauna and nibbles at plants. In the summer it feeds intensively, but passes the winter in a resting state, not feeding at all. In shallow waters which freeze down to the bottom it is able to survive, provided its body fluids do not freeze. It spawns in May and June, the female laying up to 300,000 viscous eggs on to plants.

The Crucian Carp is of more ecological than economic significance, inhabiting the kind of waters in which other species are unable to live.

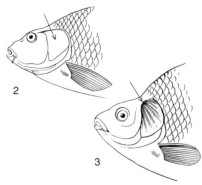

The Crucian Carp (1), unlike the Wild Carp, has a short, high body with a shorter and a blunt-ended head, the mouth being upturned and without barbels. The iris is silverish and the dorsal fin convex. Another difference from the Wild Carp (2) is the convex, wrinkled gill operculum (3). The Crucian Carp is also substantially smaller, growing to a length of 15-30 cm at a weight of 0.5-1 kg. The stunted form (4) differs from a typical high-bodied one with its low body, relatively large head and a dark spot in front of the caudal fin.

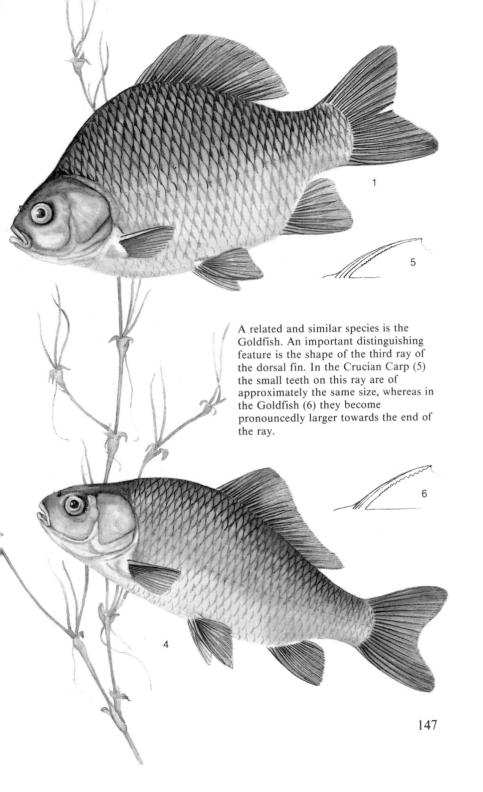

1

5

A related and similar species is the
Goldfish. An important distinguishing
feature is the shape of the third ray of
the dorsal fin. In the Crucian Carp (5)
the small teeth on this ray are of
approximately the same size, whereas in
the Goldfish (6) they become
pronouncedly larger towards the end of
the ray.

6

4

147

Goldfish
Carassius auratus

Cyprinidae

The Goldfish was brought to Europe from the Far East as an aquarium fish in the 17th century by the Portuguese. Nowadays it occurs in discreet, isolated populations in northern, central and eastern Europe, as a result of aquarium escapes, and by introduction together with herbivorous fish species. As it is often mistaken for the Crucian Carp, its exact distribution is not known, although Europe forms its western margin. It inhabits the lower reaches of large rivers, river arms with a through-flow, and larger lakes and ponds. In rivers it also lives in the current of the main stream.

It reproduces gynogenetically, the majority of the European population consisting solely of females which spawn with the males of other related species, such as carps, tenches, breams and rudds. The male sex cell of these related species, however, does not combine with the nucleus of the Goldfish egg, but penetrates the outer membrane, activates the egg to cleave and then itself perishes. The further eastwards, the greater the number of males in populations, until the normal balance of the two sexes is reached.

The Goldfish is an omnivore. It grows better than the Crucian Carp, being fished for mainly in the Danube delta and in the Far East. In places where it is not caught the population numbers increase and Goldfish compete with native economically exploited species.

The Goldfish (1) can be distinguished from the Crucian Carp by its silvery or golden colouring, the slight indentation of the dorsal and anal fins, the markedly convex shape of the gill operculum, and by the deeply receded crown of the head, above which the dorsal musculature forms a characteristic hump. When the abdominal cavity is opened, there also appears an internal difference — the black pigmentation of the lining of the abdominal cavity. It commonly grows to a length of 20-25 cm and a weight of 200-300 g. Individuals of gynogenetic populations are larger.

The golden form (2) was originally bred in China, and from this came the oldest aquarium fish in the world, the so-called Veiled Crucian (3). Long years of breeding have succeeded in producing not only colour variations, but also many bizarre shapes, such as telescopes, skygazers, lionheads, egg-shapes, comets, etc.

Wild Carp
Cyprinus carpio

Cyprinidae

The wild form of the Carp originates from the Manchurian region in China. From the rivers feeding the Black Sea, into which it was introduced, it has penetrated the areas feeding the Mediterranean and Caspian Seas, as well as the basin of the Aral Sea. It also occurs in the area feeding the Pacific Ocean from the Amur to the Burma.

It is a gregarious, thermophilic species, thriving best in the sun-warmed waters of rivers at lower altitudes. It spawns from May to July at temperatures of 15-20 °C in warmed shallows with a growth of aquatic plants, or on flooded dry land growth. A fine spawning rash appears in the males. The females stick the 50,000-1,664,000 eggs in several batches on to the plants. There are gaps of approximately a week between each laying. In spite of a relatively short development time, many eggs still fall prey to perches, chubs and ruffs, great losses being made up for by high fecundity. Even at a size of only 2 cm, the young fish seek food on the bottom, eating the larvae of chironomids and other small invertebrates, as well as parts of plants and seeds.

In European conditions, the Wild Carp will only take food in the warm season, its greatest feeding activity being at around 20 °C. When the temperature falls below 8 °C, it stops feeding and seeks out deep places, where it overwinters in a state of torpor. Its bodily processes are markedly slowed down and are maintained by its energy reserves. It uses up 5-15 per cent of its weight over the winter. The Carp is an economically valuable fish; the wild form, however, is virtually unfished nowadays in view of the low numbers of its populations.

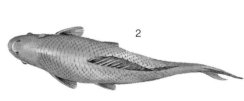

2

The Wild Carp (1) has an elongated, spindle-shaped body, terminating in a short and blunt-shaped head. Viewed from above (2), the width of the body is clearly visible, and together with its low height produces a cylindrical shape, which is adapted to movement in the swift water of rivers. It differs from the cultivated form not only in its low body, but also in its colouring. It has a dark, greenish-brown or greyish-green back,

1

3

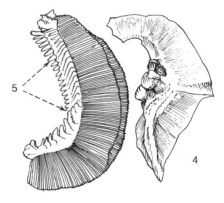

lighter, dirty olive brown sides and
a yellowish-white or creamy belly.
   Cyprinid fish have smooth, so-called
cycloid scales (3). Another characteristic
feature are the gullet teeth, which grow
on the bone of the 5th gill arch, being
arranged in three rows (4) in the case
of the Carp. The gullet teeth are
hidden among the short, thick inner
gill-rakers (5).

5

4

151

Pond Carp
Cyprinus carpio

This so-called cultivated form, which differs in many features from its wild ancestor, has been bred through long-term keeping of the Carp in artificial conditions. Carp-keeping was introduced into Europe by the Romans, from whom the tradition was taken over by monks. It was they who worked out a methodology for keeping Carp in ponds, and who distributed it throughout the whole of Europe. Pond-keeping underwent prodigious development during the Middle Ages. Most ponds were constructed so solidly and with such a knowledge of the subject of pond-keeping, that they still serve their purpose to this day.

In ponds, the Carp finds optimal conditions for its growth, commonly attaining 50-60 cm in length at a weight of 4-5 kg. Record catches measured over 1 m and weighed up to 32 kg. The growth of Carp is highly dependent on the amount of food and how much of the year it is available. For this reason it attains a larger size in the warm regions of its native waters than it does in Europe. But conditions are not uniform throughout Europe. In the south-east, for example, it attains a larger size than in the north, where because of low temperatures it may not even spawn. It can also find suitable conditions in valley reservoirs, and it has likewise penetrated rivers, from where it has actually emerged in a wild form. This fact is evidently the reason why the European Wild Carp has almost disappeared from the Danube. The last remnants of Wild Carp populations spawn together with the cultivated form and the hybrids produced tend to lose the typical features of the wild form, for example its resistance to parasites and disease. Fishermen are therefore trying by means of intentional cross-breeding to transfer these positive characteristics to the cultivated Carp, and thus increase its resistance.

The cultivated Pond Carp (1) differs conspicuously from the wild form in the shape of its body. The Pond Carp is

2

a high-bodied fish, in which the back rises steeply behind the head. The belly is often also arched. The cultivated form also differs in its colouring. The back is greyish-blue, the sides greenish or bluish, and the belly yolk-yellow or creamy white. By means of selective breeding, fishes with various types of scaling, including a scaleless form, have been obtained. This type is known as the Smooth Carp, or the Naked Carp (2).

In waters in which Carp live together

1

with Crucian Carp, cross-breeding
between these two species often occurs.
The cross-breeds, so-called
'Carp-Crucians' (3) have, as do Carp,
two pairs of small barbels, which are,
however, shorter and thinner. From the
Crucian Carp they inherit the rough
opercula and a smaller size. They attain
a length of only 20-30 cm and are
infertile.

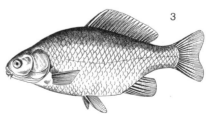

3

153

The Mirror Carp
Cyprinus carpio

Cyprinidae

Because of its tasty meat, undemanding requirements and rapid growth, the Carp is the most important freshwater fish species. The market is supplied with fish 2-4 years old and weighing 1-4 kg, when they taste best. Nevertheless, under suitable conditions, Carp can live 20-30 years, exceptionally up to 40 years.

The eggs are the basis of carp-breeding. These are obtained by means of semi-artificial spawning in small spawning ponds, the bottoms of which are sown with grasses. Before spawning, they are filled with water, and the fish spawn on the flooded growth of the bottom. Recently this traditional spawning method has been dropped, as far greater productivity is obtained through artificial spawning, in which the sexual products are carefully pressed out of the parent fish by hand, mixed together and placed into hatching apparatus. The fry are then kept in containers with a through-flow, so-called troughs. In the second year, the young Carp from both artificial and semi-artificial spawning are transferred into small ponds, and in autumn the two-year-old fish, weighing 400-800 g, are moved into the main fish ponds. There they are given extra food, and in 3-4 years, when they reach market size, they are fished out. The method described above currently has many variations. One of these is keeping Carp in waters which are heated up as a by-product of electrical power plants. The warm water prolongs the period in which the Carp take food. In spite of these new methods, however, Carp-keeping in classic ponds still predominates. The Czech Republic and France, which have the most extensive pond-keeping systems, are significant Carp producers. The annual world Carp production is 200,000 tons.

Another cultivated type of Carp is the Mirror Carp (1), which has a row of large scales on the sides of its body, a row of smaller scales along the line of the back, and sporadically smaller scales at the base of the fins. The scaleless form (2) has a row of smaller scales along the line of the back, and occasionally isolated large scales on the body or at the base of the fins.

The scales of Carps with reduced scaling (3) differ from the classic cycloid scales of scaled species (4) in their larger size and irregular shape. Bare skin without scale cover is disadvantageous for fish, since it increases the area over which parasites can take hold or an infection can enter the body. Therefore the traditional types of Carp with incomplete scaling are nowadays not being selectively bred or maintained.

2

1

3

4

Stone Moroko
Pseudorasbora parva   Cyprinidae

The Stone Moroko was unintentionally brought to Romania from China in 1960, along with herbivorous species. It is nowadays present in isolated populations in central and southern Europe and in the European part of the former USSR. Shallow, overgrown places in brooks, rivers and ponds, where it seeks refuge from predators in dense growth, suit the species. By virtue of its aggressiveness and adaptability to deteriorated conditions, it is usurping native species, and moreover competes for food with the young stages of useful fish species. It is thus both an alien and unwelcome element of competition among European fish fauna.

The Mosquito Fish (*Gambusia affinis*), belonging to the family Poeciliidae, was introduced into Europe from the southern states of the USA as a biological means for combatting mosquitoes. It lives on the latter's larvae, therefore being an effective eliminator of malaria. It is one of the species in which fertilisation takes place internally, the young developing inside the body of the mother. It is the only representative of the viviparous family to have become successfully established in Europe, where it today occurs in Spain, Italy, the Balkans, the Ukraine and the Caucasus. It can tolerate a fluctuation in temperature from 0 °C to 30 °C.

The Valencia Toothcarp, (*Valencia hispanica*), a member of the Cyprinodontidae family, is known from south-eastern and eastern Spain, Albania and the island of Corfu. It inhabits various types of water, including small pools, drainage canals and brackish water. It grows to a length of only 5-8 cm, and spawns from April to June. The young fish attain maturity within less than a year. The species is of no economic significance.

The Stone Moroko (1) grows to a length
of only 8-9 cm, rarely to 11 cm.
A characteristic feature of juvenile
individuals is a dark lateral stripe. Males
are larger than females and have longer
fins. In the spawning period they
moreover have dark colouring with
a metallic violet sheen, and several
spawning papillae in front of the eyes.

4 ♀

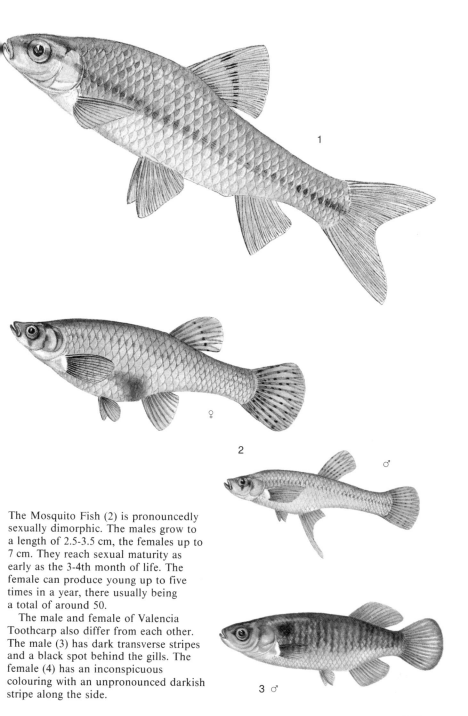

The Mosquito Fish (2) is pronouncedly sexually dimorphic. The males grow to a length of 2.5-3.5 cm, the females up to 7 cm. They reach sexual maturity as early as the 3-4th month of life. The female can produce young up to five times in a year, there usually being a total of around 50.

The male and female of Valencia Toothcarp also differ from each other. The male (3) has dark transverse stripes and a black spot behind the gills. The female (4) has an inconspicuous colouring with an unpronounced darkish stripe along the side.

157

Mediterranean Toothcarp
Aphanius fasciatus
Cyprinodontidae

The most widely distributed native European fish species of the family Cyprinodontidae is the Mediterranean Toothcarp. It is distributed in fresh and brackish waters along the coast of southern Europe, Turkey and north Africa as far as Algeria. It is an undemanding species, inhabiting various types of water, including pools, small overgrown ponds and sewers. It spawns from April to August in shallow places among the growth of aquatic plants. The fry hatch after 10-15 days and mature within a year. Their diet consists of invertebrates, mainly crustaceans and insect larvae. It is of only minor importance as an aquarium species.

Along the southern and eastern coast of Spain and at higher elevations in Algeria and Morocco lives the related species, the Iberian Toothcarp (*Aphanius iberus*). It inhabits pools, lakes, ponds, marshes and link canals, as well as mildly brackish waters. It is resistant both to fluctuations in temperature and oxygen content of the water. It spawns at water temperatures of around 24 °C. The female lays roughly 200 eggs on to aquatic plants. The fry hatch after 10-14 days and mature after 6 months. It lives on small snails, crustaceans, mosquito larvae and to some extent plants.

The Mediterranean Toothcarp (1) is a small fish, growing to only 6-7 cm. The males are larger and more colourful than the females. On the greyish-blue body of the male there are 10-15 dark transverse stripes, the fins being yellow. In the females the stripes are inconspicuous and the fins a pale greyish colour. Characteristic features of the species are the dorsal position of the mouth, and the dorsal fin, which is located towards the rear, standing almost above the anal fin. The species was not discovered and described until 1913.

2 ♂

1 ♂

♀

The Iberian Toothcarp (2) is also a small fish, growing to a length of 8 cm at most. The male is smaller than the female, measuring a maximum of 6 cm. Because of their bright colouring and conspicuous sexual dimorphism, they are popular with aquarium keepers. A striking feature of the species are the large eyes.

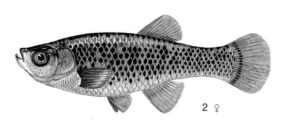

2 ♀

Spined Loach
Cobitis taenia
Cobitidae

The Spined Loach is distributed throughout almost the whole of Europe. In the north, it is absent from northern Scandinavia, Finland, the former USSR, Scotland and Wales, and in the south from Greece. It lives in clear, still waters with a slow current and a sandy bottom. It keeps mainly to shallows, where it hides during the day, buried in the sand. When in the hiding-place, the body is bent into an arch shape, so that only the head and tail protrude. Only at night does it swim out to hunt food, which consists of small bottom-dwelling fauna. By virtue of its nocturnal activity, it is only rarely caught by diurnal predatory fishes. However, it appears more frequently in the diet of nocturnal predators, for example the Eel, Eelpout or Catfish. The Spined Loach is not a particularly good swimmer, and only reluctantly leaves its hiding-place in the sand. When disturbed, it swims off with undulating movements of the whole body a short distance, once again concealing itself in the sand. It spawns from April to June. Males, unlike females, have narrowish pectoral fins, and at the base of the 2nd ray on these fins a swelling in the shape of a scale, so-called 'Canestrini's scale'. The female lays 1,000-1,500 eggs in several batches. After hatching, the fry immediately change to a life on the bottom. The Spined Loach matures in the second year of its life, living for 3-5 years. It generally grows to a length of 8-10 cm and a weight of 40-60 g. It is of no particular economic significance but because of its interesting body shape and attractive colouring, it is kept in aquaria.

In the Danube basin in former Yugoslavia, in Romania and Bulgaria, lives the related Balkan Loach (*Cobitis elongata*), which is larger than the Spined Loach, growing to a length of up to 17 cm. It lives only in flowing water.

The Spined Loach (1) has an elongated, laterally flattened body. A typical feature is the half-moon shaped dark spot on the upper side of the base of the caudal fin. Some species of the Cobitidae family have skin keels on the upper, lower, or in some cases even on both edges of the peduncle. However, the Spined Loach does not have these. Around the mouth it has three pairs of short barbels, and a double bony spine in front of each eye. The distribution and length of the barbels and the erect suborbital spines can clearly be seen when the Spined Loach's head is viewed from above (2). When in danger, for example if one takes hold of the Loach in one's hand, it erects this spine, and

2

by means of sudden movements of the body from side to side, a so-called lurch, it tries to prick the hand with the spines.

The Balkan Loach (3) differs from the Spined Loach not only in size, but also in its colouring and in the skin keel which it has on the lower side of the peduncle.

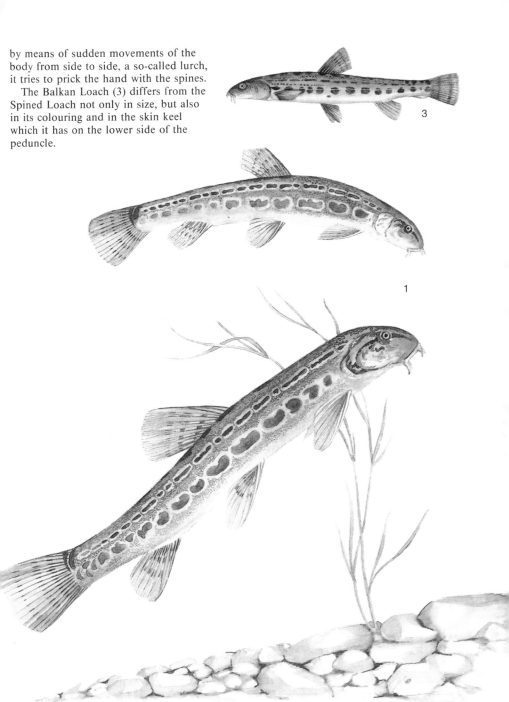

3

1

161

East European Spined Loach, Golden Loach
Cobitis aurata
Cobitidae

The East European Spined Loach is similar to its more abundant relative, the Spined Loach. The two species do not differ greatly from each other, even in size. The East European Spined Loach grows to a length of 8-12 cm, rarely up to 14 cm, and 50 g in weight. It has longish barbels around the mouth. The last pair is particularly long, reaching as far as the rear edge of the eyes. The East European Spined Loach also differs in its thicker, bony spine under the eye, and in the skin keel on the lower edge of the tail part of the body. It occurs in the river basins of the Danube, the Wisla, the Don, in some rivers of the Balkan peninsula, and outside Europe in Asia Minor and the Near East. It lives mainly in shallow and clear submontane rivers with flowing water, also occurring in suitable places of the main stream of the Danube. An essential condition for its occurrence is a hard stony bottom and a water depth of 1.5 m. During the day, it hides under stones, never burying itself in sand. In the event of disturbance, it darts out from under its cover, and with jerking leaps along the bottom seeks out the nearest hiding-place. It spawns from April until June. The female lays only 100-400 eggs. The fry, as in the case of the Spined Loach, are reminiscent of small, thin, transparent sticks. The related Rumanian Loach (*Cobitis romanica*) is similar to the previous members of the genus *Cobitis* in the colouring of its body and in its mode of life. It is known from Romania and from the upper reaches of some tributaries of the Danube.

The East European Spined Loach (1) is similar to the Spined Loach in its elongated, flat-sided body, but it differs not only in its thicker bony spine under the eye and longer barbels, but also in its colouring. The basic body colouring

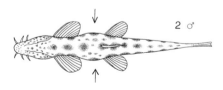

162

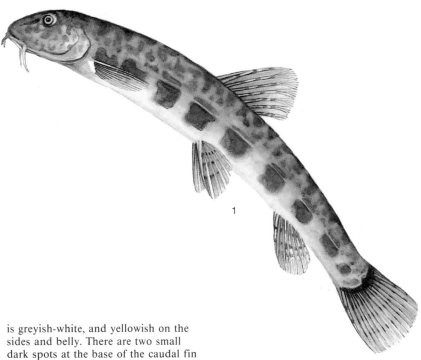

1

is greyish-white, and yellowish on the sides and belly. There are two small dark spots at the base of the caudal fin which sometimes fuse into each other to form an elongated stripe. On the sides it has irregular dark spots, the colouring, size and number of which is highly variable. Fish from calmer, lowland courses usually have a smaller number of larger spots, and vice versa. The male of the Spined Loach lacks the so-called 'Canestrini's scales' on the pectoral fins. It differs from the female in the swelling of the sides in front of the dorsal fin, which is very conspicuous when viewed from above (2).

The Rumanian Loach (3) is known from some tributaries of the upper reaches of the Danube. It has a strikingly light stripe on the sides.

3

Italian Loach
Cobitis larvata

Cobitidae

The torrents of northern Italy in the Bergantino region are inhabited by the Italian Loach. It keeps to shallow currents with a sandy and stony bottom covered with aquatic plants which grow in the flow, where it also spawns from April to June. It feeds on small bottom-dwelling invertebrates, mainly insect larvae and worms. As it grows to a length of only 5-9 cm and is not particularly abundant, it is of no economic significance.

Another species, the Venetian Loach (*Cobitis conspersa*), is known from several rivers of northern Italy, such as the Brenta and the Guay. This is another small species, 6-9 cm in length. It inhabits shallow, swift waters, where it spawns in April and June on a gravelly bottom among plants. Its diet consists of bottom invertebrate fauna.

The Caucasian Loach (*Cobitis caucasica*) occurs only in some rivers in the region between the Black and Caspian Seas, for example in the Kuma and Terek. It usually inhabits the upper reaches of courses, less frequently central ones, keeping to places with flowing water and a gravelly bottom, where there are stones and a growth of aquatic plants. It also spawns in this environment from May to June. The difference between the male and the female manifests itself in the same way as in the East European Spined Loach in the swelling of the sides in front of the dorsal fin. The diet of the Caucasian Loach consists of small bottom-dwelling fauna.

The Italian Loach (1) is identical to other representatives of the *Cobitis* genus in its basic features, differing solely in its dark, triangular spots in front of the eyes, the skin keels in the upper and lower parts of the peduncle and in the two dark spots on the peduncle in front of the caudal fin.

3

Characteristic of the Venetian Loach (2) are the two large dark spots on the back, in front of the dorsal fin, and the 3-4 smaller spots behind this fin.

The Caucasian Loach (3) is a small, 6-11 cm long fish. Unlike the previous members of the genus *Cobitis*, it does not have dark patches on its body, but a great number of small brown spots. A light stripe runs along the sides.

Weatherfish
Misgurnis fossilis

Cobitidae

In Europe, the Weatherfish inhabits rivers from the Seine to the Neva and from the Danube to the Volga, being absent from the area feeding the Arctic Ocean, rivers in England, Scandinavia and Finland and from southern Europe.

It lives in muddy, still waters, in pools, overgrown ponds and irrigation canals. It keeps to the bottom, where it also seeks its food, which consists of small invertebrates, mainly molluscs, worms and insect larvae, as well as parts of plants. It is active mainly at night, therefore escaping our attention. Only with dramatic changes in atmospheric pressure, for example before a storm, does it rise to the surface and become active even during the day. The Weatherfish has auxiliary respiration, which enables it to survive in waters with a poor supply of oxygen. Part of its gut is adapted to the transferral of oxygen into the blood. During a period of severe oxygen shortage in the water, the Weatherfish swallows air from the surface. The swallowing of air is accompanied by smacking sounds and its emission through the anal orifice, on the other hand, by whistling sounds. These sound effects can even be heard from dry land, and betray the presence of Weatherfish in apparently uninhabited waters. Auxiliary gut respiration enables Weatherfish buried in mud to survive even during the short-term periods when the water dries up in the heat of summer. The Weatherfish also survives the winter in a state of rest buried in mud.

It spawns from April to June in the growth of aquatic plants. Like other representatives of the family Cobitidae, it is of no great economic significance. Because of its interesting biology and colouring, it is sometimes kept in aquaria.

The Weatherfish (1) has an elongated, snake-like body, which is laterally flattened in the rear part. There are 10 barbels around the oral orifice, the number and location of which are characteristic for individual genera of the Cobitidae family. The Weatherfish has two pairs of longer barbels on the front edge of the upper jaw, a pair of long barbels in the corners, and two pairs of short barbels on the lower lip (2).

3

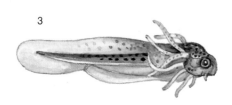

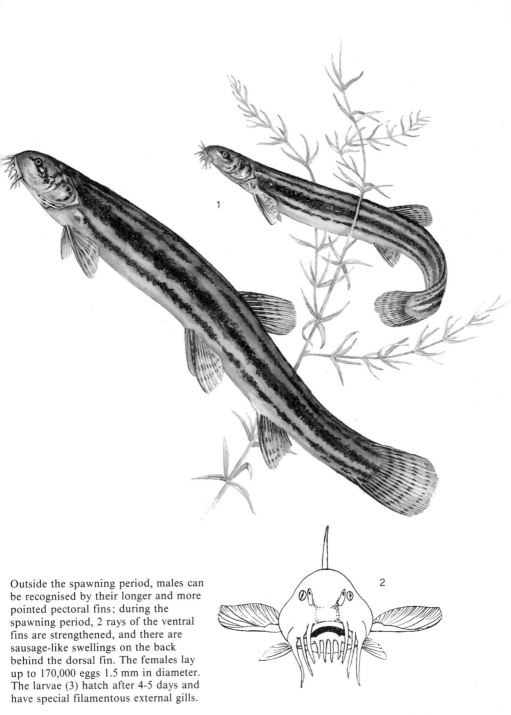

Outside the spawning period, males can be recognised by their longer and more pointed pectoral fins; during the spawning period, 2 rays of the ventral fins are strengthened, and there are sausage-like swellings on the back behind the dorsal fin. The females lay up to 170,000 eggs 1.5 mm in diameter. The larvae (3) hatch after 4-5 days and have special filamentous external gills.

167

Stone Loach
Noemacheilus barbatulus

Cobitidae

The Stone Loach is widespread in Europe and the Asian part of the former USSR, being absent from Norway, northern Sweden, northern Scotland, the Pyrenean peninsula, central and southern Italy and from Greece. It also occurs in the brackish water of some bays in the Baltic Sea. It lives in the currents of the upper and central reaches of courses and in some ponds and dams with a through-flow, where it settles in the immediate vicinity of tributaries. It will survive even in acid waters which well up from peaty soil, or in flooded quarries with hard water. Auxiliary gut respiration ensures its survival during the unfavourable conditions of summer or when the water is very muddy after rain. The Stone Loach is a bottom-dwelling species. Like all representatives of the family Cobitidae, it has a stunted swim bladder, therefore moving only along the bottom, where it swims with snakelike movements of the body. It hides during the day, leaving its refuge towards the evening and searching along the bottom. Its diet consists of small animals and remnants of aquatic plants. It reproduces during the spring months. A spawning rash appears on both sexes, being more extensive on males. Males can be distinguished even outside the period of sexual activity, unlike females having longish pectoral fins and skin borders both on the upper and lower edges of the peduncle.

In spite of the fact that the Stone Loach is relatively resistant to organic pollution of water, its numbers are declining. It forms an important dietary component of trout, and serves as bait for anglers. In the past, however, it used to be popular for its very tasty meat. To this day, it is caught in places where it is abundant and eaten by gourmets.

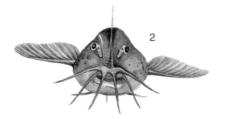

2

The Stone Loach (1) is an elongated fish with a cylindrical body and a roundish head which is flattened on top. The ventral mouth has six tactile barbels (2). Two pairs are situated on the upper lip, and one pair is in the corners of the

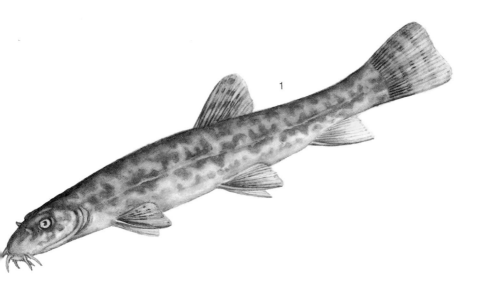

1

mouth. A typical feature of the species is the straight-edged caudal fin. The apparently smooth skin conceals small scales on the sides, which do not overlap as in most fishes, but lie freely side by side. It usually attains a length of 10-15 cm and a weight of 80-150 g, living up to 5-8 years.

The body of the Stone Loach is covered with a number of brownish spots (3) which are not sharply delineated, so that the colouring gives the impression of marbling. The result is that the contour of the body is blurred and the colouring, therefore, has a protective function.

3

Angora Loach
Noemacheilus angorae   Cobitidae

The Angora Loach occurs in some torrents, rivers and lakes feeding the Black and Aegean Seas, for example in the rivers Kamer and Coruh. It lives in shallow flowing water among stones and aquatic flora, where it also spawns from May to June. It matures at a length of 5-6 cm. It feeds on small bottom-dwelling fauna, mainly worms and insect larvae. It is a small fish, attaining only 6-8 cm, rarely 9 cm, in length. It is of no economic significance. There is a lack of detailed knowledge of its biology.

Another little-known loach species from south-eastern Europe is the Terek Loach (*Noemacheilus merga*). It lives in the torrents feeding some rivers, for example the Kuban, the Kuma, the Terek and the Samur, in the south-western part of the former USSR between the Black and Caspian Seas. It keeps to flowing water with a stony and gravelly bottom, where it also seeks its food, which consists of small benthic fauna. As with the previous species very little is known about its mode of life.

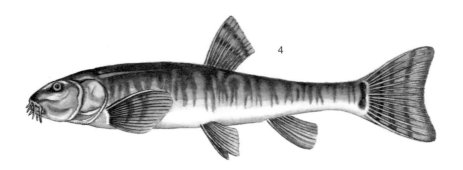

4

The Angora Loach (1) is similar to the Stone Loach in its colouring and body shape. In places where both species occur together, it is difficult to tell them apart. They differ only in the shape of the caudal fin. In the Stone Loach, the caudal fin is more straight-edged (2), whereas in Angora Loach it is slightly indented (3). The Stone Loach moreover has long, tubular nostrils.

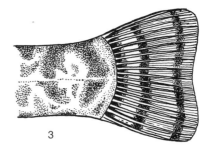

The Terek Loach (4) differs pronouncedly from the previous species in its colouring and body structure, particularly conspicuous being its long and narrow peduncle, which is almost circular in cross-section. The body, on the other hand, is rather broad and the caudal fin is indented.

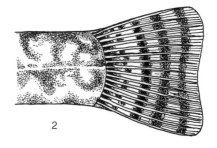

171

European Catfish, Wels
Silurus glanis

Siluridae

The European Catfish is widespread in all rivers from the upper course of the Rhine eastwards in the regions feeding the North, Baltic, Black and Caspian Seas and the Sea of Aral. The southern margin of its area of distribution is formed by the Alps, and the northern margin by Scandinavia, where it occurs only in southern Sweden. It has also been introduced into England and occurs in brackish water in bays of the Baltic, Black and Caspian Seas.

This is a thermophilic species. It inhabits rivers, lakes, valley reservoirs and larger ponds, where it seeks out deeper waters with a slow current and a soft bottom. During the day, it lies in its hiding-place, becoming active only after sunset, when it leaves the shelter and hunts for smaller fishes. In spite of being a predatory species, it does not avoid carrion. Its need for warm water has resulted in a range of spawning times throughout Europe—in central Europe from May to June, in the north from June to August. The pre-condition for spawning to occur is water warmed to around 20 °C. The female lays up to 500,000 light yellow eggs, which cling together in clusters. The male fertilises the eggs with milt, and also guards them during the 3 days it takes for them to develop. His faithfulness is proverbial. A case is known in which a sudden drop in the water level in a dam took place, and the nest was stranded almost on dry land. The male stayed as close as he was able to swim, and using the tail part of its body splashed the nest with water in order to prevent the eggs from perishing.

The European Catfish occupies an important place in pond and river fishery management. It is a useful biological-control agent regulating over-reproduction in unwanted fish species.

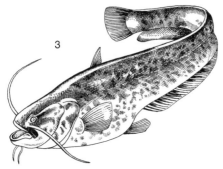

The European Catfish (1) has an elongated, smooth, scaleless body, which is reminiscent of an outsized tadpole. The robust head (2) terminates in a wide mouth. The fine, sharp teeth grow on both jaws, on the lower jaw forming a band of 4-5 rows. There are 2 long, mobile barbels on the upper lip in the corners and 4 smaller, immobile ones on the chin. The European Catfish grows to a length of 1-2 metres and a weight of

1

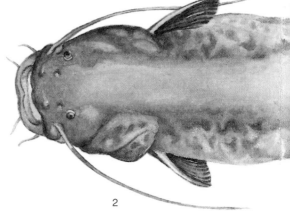

10-15 kg. In south-eastern Europe, where
conditions are better, it attains a length
of 3-4 metres at a weight of about
200 kg. A record catch from the Dnieper
measured five metres and weighed
306 kg. The European Catfish can live
up to 80 years or more.

Another European representative of
the genus is Aristotle's Catfish (*Silurus
aristotelis*) (3), which inhabits only
southern Greece. Unlike the European
Catfish, it has 4 barbels and attains
a length of only 2 metres and 150 kg
in weight.

2

Horned Pout, Brown Bullhead
Ictalurus nebulosus
Ictaluridae

The home of the Horned Pout is southern Canada and the USA, where it lives in the basins of the Great Lakes and the St. Lawrence river, and in the northern part of the USA in the basin of the river Ohio. It was brought to Europe at the end of the last century, and in some regions it has survived to this day. It occurs in rivers with a slow current, in lakes, pools and swamps and will tolerate a shortage of oxygen and poor feeding conditions. It can survive in the kind of waters in which most other fish species would perish. The Horned Pout keeps predominantly to the bottom, becoming active mainly at night. It spawns in the period from April to July at temperatures of 18-20 °C. A pair of Horned Pout builds a nest on overgrown shallows into which the female lays 1,000-13,000 cream-coloured eggs. The nest, containing the future generation, is taken care of by both parents. The fry hatch after 8 days, and remain under the supervision of both parents until they start to swim, when their care is taken over exclusively by the male. Young fish feed on small crustaceans, insect larvae, and partly also on plants. Older specimens eat eggs, fry and smaller fishes. The Horned Pout matures in its 2nd-3rd year, and can live up to eight years.

The Horned Pout was introduced into Europe with the intention of obtaining a supplementary fish species with good growth characteristics. These assumptions, however, have not proved true. In central European conditions, the Horned Pout usually grows to a length of only 15-20 cm and a weight of 100-300 g. Nowadays it is bred intensively in southern Europe, where it attains a somewhat larger size. Its meat is tasty and without bones.

3

The Horned Pout (1) is similar to the European Catfish in the shape of its body and in its colouring. Unlike the latter, however, it has eight barbels at the mouth, a shorter anal fin, and an adipose fin on the back between the dorsal and caudal fins. Outside the spawning period, the ventral side is whitish (2), turning yellow to orange in colour in the spawning period.

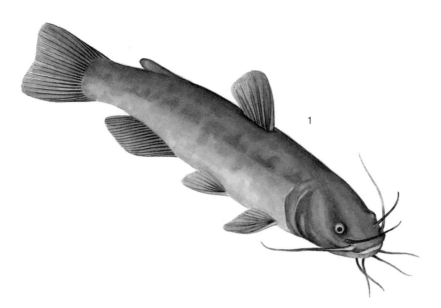

A characteristic feature of the Horned
Pout larva (3) are two pairs of barbels,
which are absent in the larva of the
European Catfish.

Another related species, the Black
Bullhead (*Ictalurus melas*), (4) was
introduced into Europe from the eastern
part of North America. It attains the
same size as the Horned Pout, that is
15-25 cm. From the economic viewpoint,
it is of minimal significance, being
caught to be kept in garden pools or in
aquaria rather than for consumption.

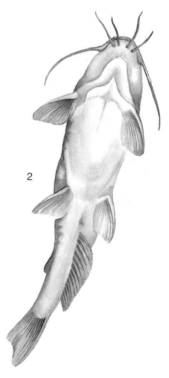

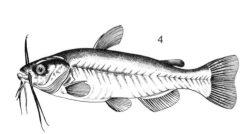

European Eel
Anguilla anguilla

Anguillidae

The European Eel is widespread along the European coast of the Atlantic Ocean, the Mediterranean and Black Seas and the Sea of Azov, as well as in courses feeding these seas. From the coast, the females actively penetrate rivers upstream, males mostly remaining in the brackish water of the estuary. The natural migration of Eels, however, is in many places impeded by dams, small eels therefore being fished in river estuaries and transported to inaccessible places. In this way, males can also reach interior waters.

Until reaching sexual maturity, Eels inhabit ponds, valley reservoirs and rivers, in which they ascend up to elevations of 1,000 m. Males mature at an age of 4-14 years, females at an age of 10-20 years. As soon as the Eel reaches sexual maturity, its back turns dark and the belly turns silvery white. At the same time it stops feeding and lives from its fat reserves. At the end of summer or the beginning of autumn, adult Eel set out downstream on the journey to the sea, where a 4,000-7,000 km long journey to the spawning site awaits them. During this trip they must cover a distance of 20-40 km each day. In March to April they spawn in the Sargasso Sea between the Bahamas and Bermuda. Spawning is collective, occurring at depths of 100-400 m over a sea-depth of 6 km. After spawning, adult individuals perish from exhaustion and their dead bodies sink to the depths. The hatched larvae drift passively in the Gulf Stream, which carries them within three years to the shores of Europe.

The European Eel (1) has a snake-like body. The ventral fins are absent and the dorsal, caudal and anal fins join into a continuous border. The skin is fine, and scales only start to appear in the third year of its life. In European waters, there occurs a larger, broad-headed form (2), which probably constitutes females, and a smaller, narrow-headed one (3), which is probably that of the males.

The letters on the map indicate the distance from the site of spawning and correspond to the number of larval developmental stages.

a—Freshly hatched larvae are elongated and measure 5-7 mm, b—after two months they measure 25 mm and change their shape, c—after 8 months they measure 45 mm and are reminiscent of transparent willow leaves, d—after a year and a half they attain a maximum size of 75 mm, e—at the age of two and a half years the size of a larva starts to decrease to 70 mm and the body narrows, f—when they reach the coast of Europe the larvae have already metamorphosed into small Eels.

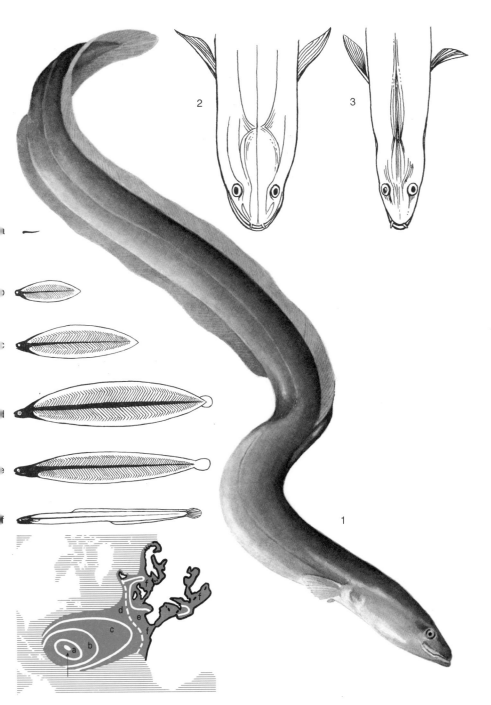

Burbot
Lota lota
Gadidae

The Burbot is widespread in northern Europe, with the exception of the greater part of England and Norway. The southern border of its distribution is formed by the north of the Balkan and Pyrenean peninsulas and in Italy by the basin of the river Po. It inhabits predominantly the upper and central reaches of rivers, valley reservoirs and some ponds with a through-flow. It requires cool water, rich in oxygen and with a sufficient number of hiding-places, from which it swims out only towards evening or at night to seek food.

As a species of Arctic origin, the Burbot is most active in autumn and winter, when most feeding takes place and energy reserves are built up. In the heat of summer, when its activity decreases and it falls into the so-called summer sleep, the fat reserves in the liver are digested. Unlike most European fish species, it spawns in winter from December to March at water temperatures ranging from 0 °C to 6 °C. In spite of high female fecundity (up to 3,000,000 eggs), the numbers of juvenile fry are not particularly high. Part of the fault in this lies with the Burbot itself, as it intensively eats both its own eggs and fry.

The main Burbot diet consists of fishes and their fry, frogs, larvae, aquatic insects and molluscs. In cool regions, the period of feeding activity is prolonged, this being the reason why record catches come, for example, from Siberia, where Burbot can attain a weight of 25-32 kg. The usual size of catches in European conditions is 60-70 cm and 2-5 kg. The meat and liver of the Burbot are very tasty. In spite of this fact, however, it is not economically important, as it is difficult to catch, being active mostly at night.

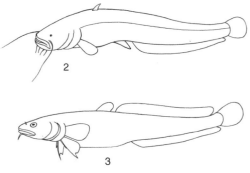

2

3

The Burbot (1) has a cylindrical body which narrows towards the tail, and a broad head which is flattened on top and has a big toothed mouth. The body is covered with smooth skin, in which there are small scales scattered irregularly and deeply ingrown.

It is frequently mistaken for the Catfish. Unlike the Catfish (2), however, the Burbot (3) has two dorsal fins and the pectoral fins are situated under the ventral ones. It has one barbel in the middle of the chin. Both species swim

by means of undulation of the whole body, like the Eel. The Burbot helps itself along by undulating the long second dorsal fin.

The closest related species to the Burbot is the Ling (*Molva molva*) (4), which lives in the sea along the coast of the northern Atlantic. Unlike the Burbot, however, it does not have tubular, elongated and protruding nostrils or pores of the lateral line on the head.

1

4

Three-spined Stickleback
Gasterosteus aculeatus
Gasterosteidae

The Three-spined Stickleback is widespread along the Atlantic coast from Iceland and northern Norway to the Mediterranean and Black Seas. It has also been introduced into many inland waters by aquarists, for example into the Vltava. From the coast it often penetrates naturally into both brackish and fresh water, creating permanent populations in coastal lakes with fresh water. Most coastal populations overwinter in the sea, and early in spring migrate to rivers to spawn. In the spawning period from March to June, the male builds a nest with an entrance on the bottom made of plant fragments glued together by his kidney excretions. By means of complex ritual movements, he entices a female to the nest; the female lays the 60-600 eggs, piercing a new opening and swimming off. The male then swims into the nest and fertilises the eggs, after which he entices other females to the nest. As a result the nest can contain up to 1,000 eggs. The male Three-spined Stickleback is a textbook example of a guardian fish. He not only guards the nest but also takes care of the eggs, keeping them supplied with oxygen. As there are eggs from several females in the nest, the fry hatch in 2-4 batches. After hatching, they keep to the nest and its vicinity for approximately one week, being constantly guarded by the male. They mature as early as the end of the first year of life. The Three-spined Stickleback can live to a maximum of 4 years. Because of its interesting mode of reproduction, it is often kept in aquaria.

Within its range the Three-spined Stickleback overlaps with the Nine-spined Stickleback (*Pungitius pungitius*). It inhabits the fresh waters of pools, ponds and rivers, as well as the brackish waters of river estuaries and sea bays. It attains a maximum length of 9 cm.

The Three-spined Stickleback (1) grows to a length of 6-8 cm, rarely up to 11 cm. A typical feature are the three free spines in front of the dorsal fin. During the breeding season the front part of the lower body of males turns orange-red to vivid red, the back turning metallic blue and the gills golden. The female, however, only develops a more vivid silvery colouring and a roundish belly. In Three-spined Sticklebacks from brackish waters, the rows of bony platelets on the sides (2) are well-developed. In freshwater populations, there are only a few of these or none at all (3).

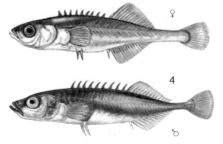

Despite the Nine-spined Stickleback's name (4) indicating nine spines, this number is not the rule: the number of free spines in front of the dorsal fin ranges from 7 to 11. It has no bony platelets on its sides. In the breeding season, both males and females retain their basic colouring but the colours become more intense.

Broadnose Pipefish
Syphonostoma typhle

Syngnathidae

The Broadnose Pipefish is distributed along the Atlantic coast of Europe southwards from Norway, as well as in the Baltic, Mediterranean and Black Seas and the Sea of Azov. It lives in coastal shallows and lower reaches of rivers, where it hunts its food, which consists of invertebrates, mainly small crustaceans and fry. It spawns from March to August. In mature males a brood pouch for the rearing of fry forms on the lower part of the body behind the cloaca. The Broadnose Pipefish reaches maturity in its second year and lives up to four years. It is of no economic significance but is notable for its interesting body morphology, therefore often being kept by aquarists. In places where it occurs in substantial numbers it constitutes food for predatory fishes and dolphins of the *Tarsiops tursic* species.

Unlike the Broadnose Pipefish, the female Straight-nosed Pipefish (*Nerophis ophidion*) does not deposit eggs into the brood pouch of the male, as this is absent in the males of this species. Instead, during spawning she sticks the 50-300 eggs on to his belly. The male then carries these there until they hatch. The Straight-nosed Pipefish matures in its second year, living to an age of only three years. It attains a length of 15-25 cm, sometimes even 30 cm; males are smaller than females. It lives along the European coast from northern Norway to the Mediterranean and Black Seas and north-west Africa. It also enters the lower reaches of rivers, for example the Dnieper and Dniester. It is of no economic significance, although it constitutes food for some fish species.

The body of the Broadnose Pipefish (1) is covered with bony skin platelets, forming hexagonal rings on the pectoral and ventral parts and square rings on the tail part. The snout (2) is flat-sided. The colouring of the body ranges from shades of green to brown. The

Broadnose Pipefish grows to a length of 20-30 cm, rarely up to 37 cm. During spawning (3) the pair press the abdominal parts of their bodies against each other and the female deposits the 150-200 eggs into the male's brood pouch by means of her ovipositor. The brood pouch then closes and the male rears the eggs in it for 25-30 days. Prior to hatching the brood pouch splits lengthwise and the fry spill out into the water.

The Straight-nosed Pipefish (4) has an elongate body which is round in cross-section, and lacks the pectoral fins

2

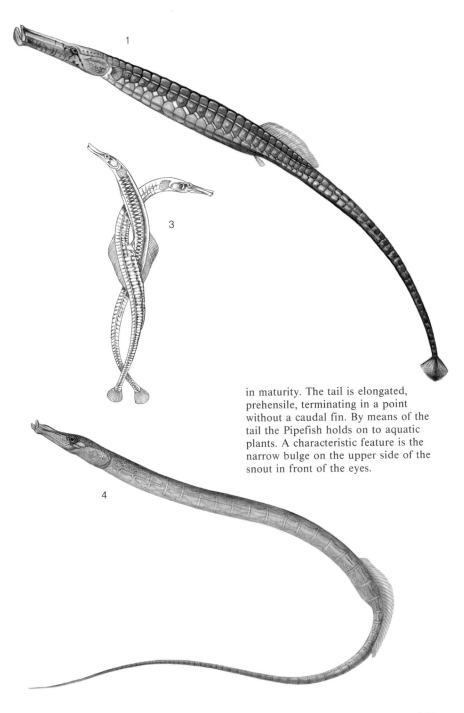

in maturity. The tail is elongated,
prehensile, terminating in a point
without a caudal fin. By means of the
tail the Pipefish holds on to aquatic
plants. A characteristic feature is the
narrow bulge on the upper side of the
snout in front of the eyes.

Common Mullet, Striped Mullet
Mugil cephalus
Mugilidae

The largest and economically most important mullet is the Common Mullet. It is distributed in a wide belt along the Atlantic coast of southern Europe, the Black Sea and the Sea of Azov, and near the coast of North America. Like other mullets it adapts well to a variable salt content in water, therefore not being limited only to sea water. It does live mostly in the sea, however, where it undertakes lengthy food and spawning migrations. It spawns from June to August. The eggs are pelagic, and much danger lies in wait for them, the females therefore having enormous fecundity, from 3,000,000 to 7,000,000 eggs. Young fish move to fresh and brackish waters in early spring, returning to the sea in autumn. They reach maturity relatively late, males at 6-7 years, females a year later. They generally attain a length of 40-60 cm and a weight of 5-6 kg.

Golden spots behind the eyes and on the opercula are typical for the Golden Grey Mullet (*Mugil auratus*). It inhabits the Atlantic coast of Europe and Africa, as well as the Black Sea and the Sea of Azov, and has also been successfully introduced into the Caspian Sea. From salt and brackish water it sometimes penetrates the lower reaches of rivers, for example in the Dnieper. It spends most of its life in the sea, where it spawns from August to September. The eggs are pelagic. The Golden Grey Mullet matures in its 4-5th year. It lives mainly on filamentous algae and plant detritus, as well as occasionally on small bottom-dwelling invertebrates. The meat of the Golden Grey Mullet is tasty. It is fished on a large scale mainly in the Mediterranean and Black Seas, sometimes also being caught with rod and line.

The Common Mullet (1) has an elongate, torpedo-like body, covered with large cycloid scales. A striking feature are the two separate dorsal fins and the high location of the pectoral

fins. An important distinguishing characteristic is the positioning of the eyes in deep sockets. On its sides it has 7-10 greenish-brown, lengthwise stripes, among which flash golden to light blue

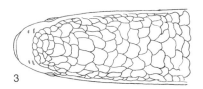

3

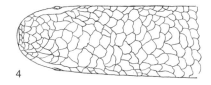

4

shades. The Golden Grey Mullet (2) has a torpedo-like, slightly laterally flattened body. The head is flat on top and terminates in a large mouth, the lower jaw of which is covered with scales. It has 6-7 dark lengthwise stripes along the sides.

The scales in mullets reach as far as the head. From above it is easy to tell the difference between the Golden Grey Mullet (3), in which the scales reach only as far as the nostrils, and the Common Mullet (4), in which the scales also cover the upper jaw.

Grey Mullet
Mugil labeo

Mugilidae

The Grey Mullet is distributed along the coastal belt of Europe from France and Great Britain to Greece.

Like other European mullets, this is an active pelagic fish, inhabiting muddy coastal shallows. In the summer months it penetrates the brackish water of coastal lakes and the estuaries of great rivers, as well as the fresh water of their lower reaches. There it seeks out mainly shallow backwaters with rich aquatic plant growth. It lives on detritus and outgrowths of aquatic plants on the bottom, as well as small fauna living in these outgrowths. Using its mouth, it scrapes food from the bottom, sucking it in together with water. It filters food through the dense filter of the gill-rakers, on to which are caught plant fragments and small fauna. It grinds the morsels with its pharyngeal teeth, spitting out indigestible remnants. The food is further processed in the thick-walled muscular stomach and the very long gut. As the plant components predominate in its diet, the food is not very nutritious, its value having to be compensated for by bulk. Mullets thus feed intensively both day and night, the gut being 4-5 times the length of the body.

The Grey Mullet spawns in the sea from July to September. The eggs are pelagic and usually total several million. It is of economic significance mainly along the coast of France.

The Grey Mullet (1) is a small species, growing to a length of only 15-20 cm, rarely up to 25 cm. It has a torpedo-shaped body with large cycloid scales extending as far as the head. The dorsal fin is divided into two separate sections, the first of which has four hard rays. The lower lip is conspicuous, being smooth and its thickness being equal to the diameter of the eye.

The Grey Mullet and the Common Mullet can be distinguished by the formation of the gap between the bones of the lower jaw. In the Grey Mullet (2) this gap is of a narrow, arrow-like shape, whereas in the Common Mullet (3) it is broader and more oval.

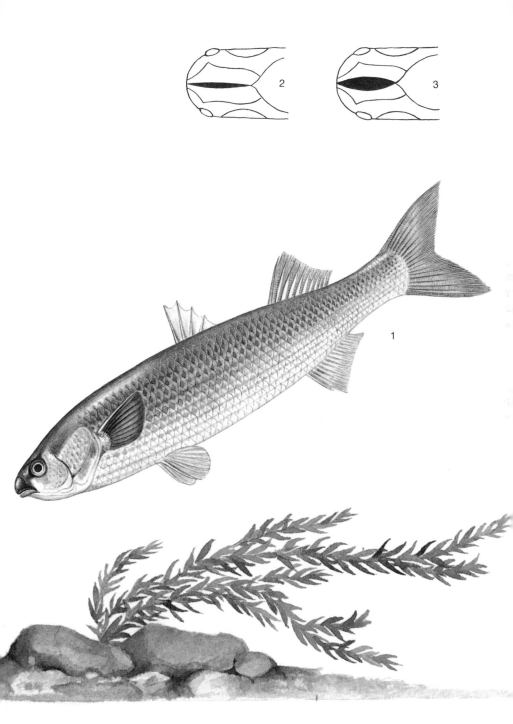

2   3

1

Thin-lipped Grey Mullet
Mugil capito

Mugilidae

The Thin-lipped Grey Mullet lives along the Atlantic coast of Europe and Africa from southern Norway to the Cape of Good Hope, as well as in the Mediterranean and Black Seas. It is rare in northern latitudes. It likes to enter the fresh water of rivers, penetrating quite far upstream in them, for example up the Nile as far as Cairo. In addition to rivers, it also occurs in lakes and coastal lagoons. It is the most abundant mullet species in European fresh waters. It spawns in the sea, usually at night. Males predominate in spawning shoals, being smaller than the females. As an active pelagic species, it undertakes not only spawning, but also feeding migrations. It eats mainly plants but occasionally also small molluscs. It has tasty meat, and the salted roes together with the roes of other mullets form a cheap substitute for real caviare.

Another species of substantial economic significance is the Sharpnose Mullet (*Mugil saliens*). This is distributed along the Atlantic coast of southern Europe as far as the Bay of Biscay, along the western coast of Africa, as well as in the Mediterranean and Black Seas and the Sea of Azov. Together with the Golden Grey Mullet it has been successfully introduced into the Caspian Sea. It is an active pelagic species which undertakes feeding migrations during the year. During the summer months particularly, when they feed most, mullets congregate in bays and coastal lakes, often penetrating the lower reaches of rivers. Spawning takes place in the sea from June to September, the eggs being pelagic, abundant in numbers and floating on the surface.

The Thin-lipped Mullet (1) has a torpedo-shaped body covered with large cycloid scales reaching as far as the head — on top as far as the nostrils and underneath covering the lower jaw.

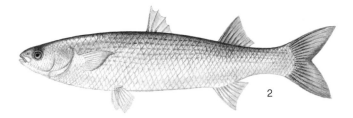

2

The body is ovoid in cross-section, but less regular than in the Golden Grey Mullet. The pectoral fins are relatively short compared with other mullet species. The body colouring is greyish-blue with a metallic sheen, a golden spot being absent on the operculum. The Thin-lipped Mullet is a relatively large species, growing to a length of 30-50 cm and a weight of 1-2 kg. Sporadically, catches attain a length of up to 70 cm and a weight of 3 kg.

The Sharpnose Mullet (2) does not differ from other mullet species in its body shape, although the head is more sharply pointed when viewed from above. It has several golden spots on the operculum. It grows to a length of 15-20 cm, in the Caspian Sea 20-35 cm, rarely attaining a size of up to 40 cm and a weight of up to 1.5 kg.

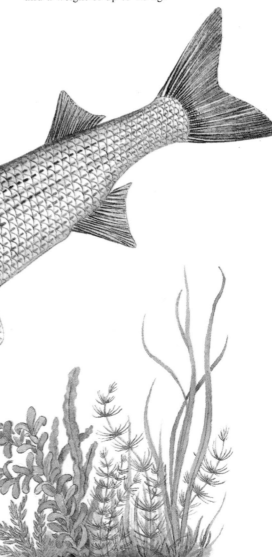

1

Thick-lipped Grey Mullet
Mugil labrosus
Mugilidae

The Thick-lipped Grey Mullet is distributed along the Atlantic coast of Europe and Africa from southern Norway as far as Senegal, as well as in the Mediterranean Sea. It also appears near the coast of Iceland, Madeira, the Canary Islands and the Azores. It occurs sporadically in the Black Sea and the lower reaches of rivers.

The Thick-lipped Grey Mullet undertakes lengthy feeding migrations, journeying northwards in spring and southwards in autumn. Like other mullets, it is a bottom feeder, gathering food in coastal shallows. The fact that mullets eat detritus means that they do not compete with other numerous fish species for food. The introduction of mullets into reservoirs where species with similar feeding requirements do not live is therefore usually successful. The Common Mullet, Golden Grey Mullet and Thin-lipped Mullet, for example, have been successfully introduced into the Caspian Sea, the latter two species not only having survived, but also even having attained a larger size than in the places of their original distribution. During the period of spawning, from June to August, the food intake in the Thick-lipped Grey Mullet is reduced. The fry hunt zooplankton and, as they orient by sight when hunting, they feed exclusively in the daytime.

The Thick-lipped Grey Mullet matures in its 3rd-5th year, growing to a length of 50-75 cm at a weight of 2-4 kg, in isolated cases up to 90 cm and 9 kg. It is an economically significant species for commercial fishing, both in the Mediterranean Sea and in northern European waters.

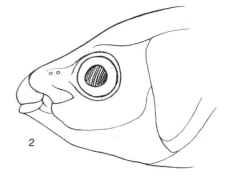

As its name implies, the characteristic feature of the Thick-lipped Grey Mullet (1) is the strikingly thick, high upper lip, the height of which is greater than half the diameter of the eye. The lower side of the lip is covered with wart-like papillae. The different formation of the lips in the Thick-lipped Grey Mullet (2)

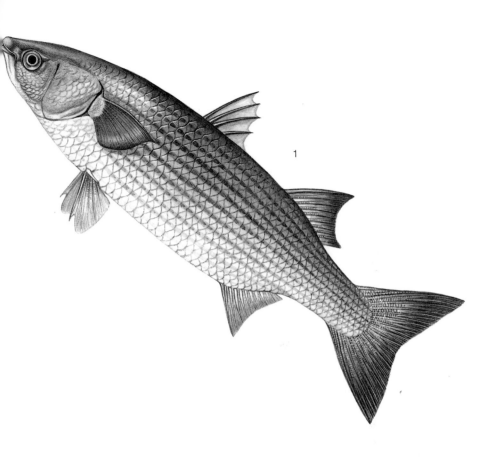

1

becomes apparent when compared, for example, with the Golden Grey Mullet (3). The mouth is small, the end not nearly reaching the front edge of the eye. There are adipose lids on the eyes of mullets. In the Thick-lipped Grey Mullet these are poorly developed and only on the front and rear edges of the eye. The Thick-lipped Grey Mullet has a dark green to blue back and silvery blue sides. On the sides it has 7-8 dark grey lengthwise stripes. The large cycloid scales reach as far as the head, but do not cover the lower jaw.

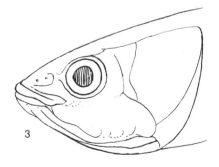

3

Boyer's Sand Smelt
Atherina mochon
Atherinidae

Boyer's Sand Smelt is present in the Mediterranean and Black Seas and the Sea of Azov, in the lower reaches of some rivers, for example the Dnestr and Bug, and in the coastal lakes of Italy and Spain, for example in the Albufera. It inhabits deepish places along the coast, migrating to shallow and overgrown coastal bays to spawn. The largest and oldest females reach the spawning sites first. The spawning of up to 2,000 eggs takes place gradually in several batches with intervals of several days between. The eggs have an attaching tendril inside with which they catch on to plants. Boyer's Sand Smelt is of no great economic importance. It grows to a length of only 10-15 cm and a maximum of 16 cm. In view of its great abundance, it is usually caught for use as feed for domestic animals. It also constitutes food for predatory fishes.

Both in its body shape and colouring the Atlantic Sand Smelt (*Atherina presbyter*) is similar to Boyer's Sand Smelt. It is somewhat larger, attaining a length of 12-15 cm and a weight of 50-70 g, rarely up to 22 cm, and a weight of 110 g. It occurs in great numbers in coastal waters from Denmark and northern England to Spain, as well as the Atlantic coast of Africa as far south as Senegal. From the sea it migrates to the brackish and fresh waters of river estuaries and coastal lakes. It spawns in sea water in shallows among aquatic plants in the period from April to July. Its eggs also attach themselves on to plants by means of tendrils. It is of the same commercial importance as Boyer's Sand Smelt.

Another related species is the Sand Smelt (*Atherina hepsetus*), which is known from the Mediterranean, Black and Caspian Seas and the Sea of Azov, as well as from the estuaries of the large rivers which feed them.

2

192

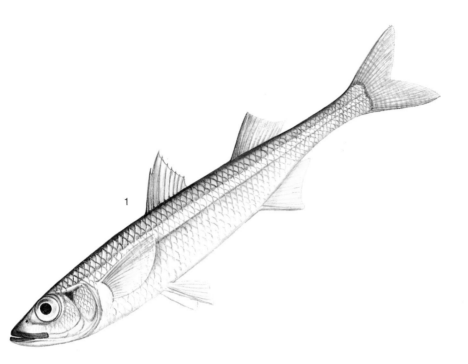

Boyer's Sand Smelt (1) has en elongate, slender body with two dorsal fins and striking large eyes. A silvery stripe, which has a width of one row of scales, runs along the sides. The scales are cycloid and bordered with black. A characteristic feature of the species is the location of the first dorsal fin, which starts above the point where the tip of the pectoral fin reaches, at the same time being above the base of the ventral fins.

The Atlantic Sand Smelt (2) also has an elongate, thin body with two dorsal fins, covered with cycloid scales. The back of the body is green in colour and the scales are bordered in black. Along the sides runs a distinct silvery band, the belly side of the body similarly being silvery white.

The Sand Smelt (3) has small scales. The silvery band along the sides is wider than one row of scales.

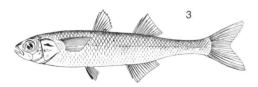

Perch
Perca fluviatilis
Percidae

The Perch occurs throughout Europe, with the exception of Scotland, Norway and south-eastern peninsulas. It inhabits the most varied types of water, ranging from pools in the upper reaches of rivers, torrents and brooks to ponds and valley reservoirs. It spawns in shoals from April to June in places with a depth of 1-4 m. Young fish live predominantly on zooplankton, later on small invertebrates, changing over to a predatory mode of life when reaching 20 cm in length. They eat smaller fishes, including their own fry. Perch spend almost the whole of their lives in shoals, hunting for food also being collective and organised. A group of Perch surrounds and circles a shoal of small fish. The Perch then rush into the shoal and hunt individual fish by means of sudden darts. Old fish, which live solitarily, hunt using another method. Like the Pike, they live in ambush for prey. When a shoal of fish carelessly approaches a Perch lying in wait, the latter darts out of its hiding place. If it does not succeed in hunting down its prey by darting, it tries pursuing it. In this it differs from the Pike, which never pursues its prey after an unsuccessful attack. In enclosed reservoirs, Perch after a time reproduce to such an extent that the food supplies are not sufficient and the population becomes stunted. Under favourable conditions, they mature at a length of 12-15 cm at the age of 2-3 years. The Perch is a long-lived fish and can live up to 50 years. Large, old fish are predominantly females.

The Perch is a favourite fish among anglers. In pond management, it has the benefit of being a market fish, as well as acting as a regulator eliminating smaller specimens of unwanted species.

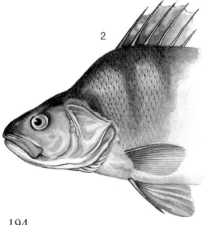

The Perch (1) usually attains 30-40 cm in length and 0.5-2 kg in weight, rarely reaching 50 cm and 5 kg. It has a wedge-shaped head with a terminal, well-toothed mouth and large, conspicuous eyes. The two dorsal fins are distinctly separate. The first is formed by hard, sharp fin rays, and there is a black spot on its rear end. This spot can even be found on young Perch, and enables it to be distinguished from young Pike-perch. The ventral fins of Percidae fishes are located under the pectoral fins. Old Perch (2) from a size of 25-30 cm have a characteristic hump,

which is formed by an abrupt arching of
the dorsal part just above the head. The
eggs (3) are enclosed in transparent,
ribbon-like coatings and form clusters.
The ribbons can be 1-2 m long.

195

Pike-perch
Stizostedion lucioperca

Percidae

The Pike-perch originally inhabited the region from the Elbe to rivers flowing into the Aral Sea, also occurring in the south in the river Maritsa and rivers in the Caucasus. From these places it has been introduced into a significant part of western Europe and the USA. It lives in smallish shoals near the bottom of deeper places in central and lower river courses. It shows a preference for places with a sandy or stony bottom and sufficient hiding-places, where it spends the day. It will even tolerate brackish waters and artificial reservoirs. It is active mainly towards evening and early in the morning.

With the exception of semi-migratory populations from brackish waters, the Pike-perch does not undertake lengthy migrations to the spawning site. As long as it can find suitable spawning conditions in its home reach, it will spawn directly there. Females lay 180,000-1,850,000 eggs, which are viscous and adhere to the bottom, as well as on to the roots of aquatic plants cleaned by the male. The male guards the deposit of eggs and takes care of them. The fry hatch after 5-10 days. After starting to swim they feed on planktonic organisms, changing over to a predatory mode of nutrition after reaching a length of 3-5 cm. At first they hunt fry, later small fish species, chiefly Bleak, Roach, Rudd, Perch and Ruffe. It is not able to swallow larger prey, as it has a small gullet.

The fact that the Pike-perch hunts less economically valuable species, the food they provide being converted to its own, very tasty meat, is the reason for great interest on the part of fishermen. Yearly catches in Europe exceed 10,000 tons. As an auxiliary fish species in ponds, it fulfils the same function as the Pike by eliminating unwanted fishes.

The Pike-perch (1), unlike the related Perch, has a slender, elongate body shape. The lateral line reaches as far as the caudal fin, the upper jaw extending behind the hind edge of the eye, and the ventral fins being further apart. It grows to a length of up to 1 m and a weight of 15 kg.

2

The East European Pike-perch (*Stizostedion volgense*) (2) is limited in its distribution solely to tributaries of the Black and Caspian Seas. It differs from the Pike-perch in its smaller size and more conspicuous transverse striping, which does not disintegrate into spots.

Pronounced features for distinguishing the two species are to be found on the head. The Pike-perch (3) has a scaleless operculum, and in the mouth has several strikingly larger, so-called dog teeth. The East European Pike-perch (4) has the operculum covered with scales and all the teeth are of approximately the same size.

Zingel
Zingel zingel
Percidae

The Zingel occurs in rivers feeding the Danube and the Dniestr, living on a gravelly bottom in the current of the main riverbed. During the day it hides under stones and in hollows in the bottom. As it does not have a swim bladder, it moves with leaping movements along the bottom. It also hunts its food on the bottom, this consisting of invertebrates, and in the spawning period the eggs and fry of other fish species. From March to May it spawns in the mild current of shallow places in the main riverbed. The female lays up to 5,000 eggs. According to some authors, she buries them in the bottom, like salmonid species. In view of its low numbers, the Zingel is of no particular economic significance. Its occurrence is becoming increasingly rare, and in some countries it has been included among protected animal species.

The Streber (*Zingel streber*) has a distribution similar to that of the related Zingel. Apart from rivers feeding the Danube and Dniestr, it also occurs in the Prut and Vardar and their tributaries. Compared to the Zingel it has higher requirements with regard to water quality. Most critical are its purity and oxygen content, and it therefore lives in the barbel zone further upstream. It seeks out deeper, swifter parts with a stony bottom. Prior to spawning a spawning rash appears in both sexes on the head, back and pectoral fins. Despite this it is still possible to distinguish males by their greater number of tubercles. The female lays the 600-4,200 viscous eggs on stones or on the gravelly bottom. Other aspects of the mode of life, including the composition of its diet, are similar to those of the Zingel. If one compares the abundance of the two species, the Streber is even more rare than the Zingel, and therefore deserves to be strictly protected.

The Zingel (1) is a slender, elongate fish with a cylindrical body and a head which is flattened on top. The two dorsal fins are markedly separate. It has a small, ventral mouth. In contrast with the related Streber, it has less conspicuous transverse striping and the tail part of the body is shorter. It grows

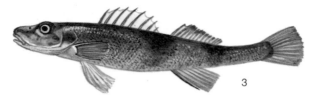

3

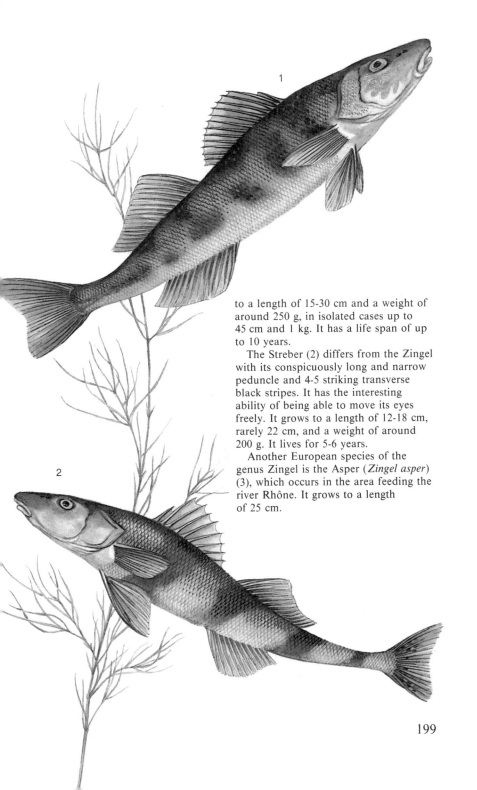

to a length of 15-30 cm and a weight of
around 250 g, in isolated cases up to
45 cm and 1 kg. It has a life span of up
to 10 years.

The Streber (2) differs from the Zingel
with its conspicuously long and narrow
peduncle and 4-5 striking transverse
black stripes. It has the interesting
ability of being able to move its eyes
freely. It grows to a length of 12-18 cm,
rarely 22 cm, and a weight of around
200 g. It lives for 5-6 years.

Another European species of the
genus Zingel is the Asper (*Zingel asper*)
(3), which occurs in the area feeding the
river Rhône. It grows to a length
of 25 cm.

Ruffe, Pope
Gymnocephalus cernua

Percidae

The Ruffe lives in the lower reaches of rivers in swift water, in dams and in some ponds, from England and north-eastern France as far as the river Kolyma in the Siberian part of Russia. It is absent from Ireland, Scotland, western and northern Norway and southern peninsulas. In spite of its relatively high demands in terms of water purity and oxygen content, it is very abundant in some places. It gathers in shoals and in April and May it enters shallows for spawning. As in the case of the Perch, the eggs are joined together in ribbon-like formations up to 1 m in length. After digesting the yolk-sac, the larvae live on small plankton and benthos, juvenile fishes on bottom-dwelling fauna, and during the breeding season of other fish species on their eggs and fry. It is therefore regarded by fishermen as an undesirable species.

In its mode of life, the Schraetzer or Striped Ruffe (*Gymnocephalus schraetzer*) resembles the Ruffe. Unlike the latter, however, it prefers deeper places with a more powerful current, where it also spawns. It occurs exclusively in the Danube from Bavaria to the estuary, as well as in the lower parts of its tributaries. The female lays up to 10,000 eggs. It only leaves the depths at night, when it swims out for food. In view of its small numbers, it is of no commercial importance.

First discovered in 1907 in the main stream of the Danube was Balon's Ruffe (*Gymnocephalus baloni*), which was initially considered to be a hybrid of the Ruffe and the Perch. It was later given full species status in 1974. The only ruffe species inhabiting the swift-flowing waters of the Arges and Vislan rivers in the area feeding the Danube in Romania is the Asprete (*Romanichthys valsanicola*), which was also described for the first time in 1974.

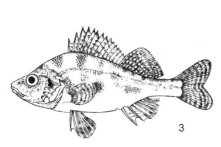

The Ruffe (1) has a short, laterally flattened body with an arched back. The operculum terminates in a conspicuous spine. The lower edge of the gills is toothed. It differs from the related Perch in having the two dorsal fins joined. It grows to a length of 12-15 cm, rarely up to 24 cm, and a weight of 100-150 g. Larger specimens are rare and tend to occur rather in the eastern part of the Ruffe's range.

The Schraetzer or Striped Ruffe (2) has a lower, more elongate body. The scales are smaller than on the Ruffe.

3

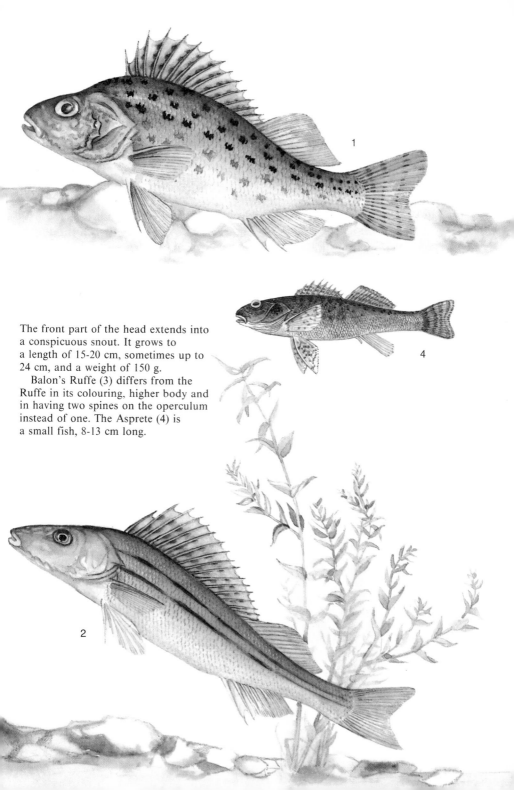

The front part of the head extends into
a conspicuous snout. It grows to
a length of 15-20 cm, sometimes up to
24 cm, and a weight of 150 g.
   Balon's Ruffe (3) differs from the
Ruffe in its colouring, higher body and
in having two spines on the operculum
instead of one. The Asprete (4) is
a small fish, 8-13 cm long.

Largemouth Bass
Micropterus salmoides   Centrarchidae

The Largemouth Bass was brought to Europe at the end of the last century from southern Canada and the USA in the hope that it would add to the number of fish species used both for economic and sport purposes. This introduction, however, has not fulfilled its purpose. The Largemouth Bass grows in its new environment to a smaller size, and moreover competes for food with native predatory species. In Europe it has so far held its own in most western European countries, and in the east in the area feeding the Danube. There it reaches sexual maturity in 3-4 years and can live up to 15 years. It is a predator: apart from fishes and aquatic insects, it also hunts frogs and tadpoles. In its native waters it is a valuable fish both to the economy and to sport fishing. In European waters it tends to be rather an unwanted fish, although not being particularly abundant.

The related Smallmouth Bass (*Micropterus dolomieu*) was introduced from North America into Europe at the end of the last century, together with the Largemouth Bass. In Europe is has only survived in a few countries, for example in France and the former USSR. In western Europe, anglers use this species to populate shallow, otherwise unusable small ponds, or keep it in some ponds as an auxiliary fish together with the Carp.

From the eastern part of North America, another species of this family — the Pumpkin-seed Sunfish (*Lepomis gibbosus*) — was brought to Europe at the end of the last century. Because of its bright colouring, which it retains even outside the breeding season, it used to be kept in ornamental park and garden reservoirs, as well as in aquaria. Nowadays it occurs only in isolated populations in western, central and eastern Europe.

The Largemouth Bass (1) in Europe usually attains a length of 30-35 cm, rarely up to 50 cm, and a weight of 1-2.5 kg. In North America it grows to a length of up to 80 cm and a weight of 4-8 kg. A typical feature, also of other species of the family, is the single dorsal fin, the front part of which is lower than the rear part. It has a large, well-toothed mouth. The rough scales extend as far as the gills. The colouring is highly variable and in adult fish there is a dark stripe along the sides. The Smallmouth Bass (2) attains a larger size in Europe than

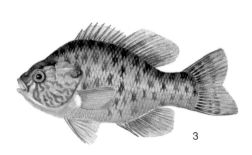

3

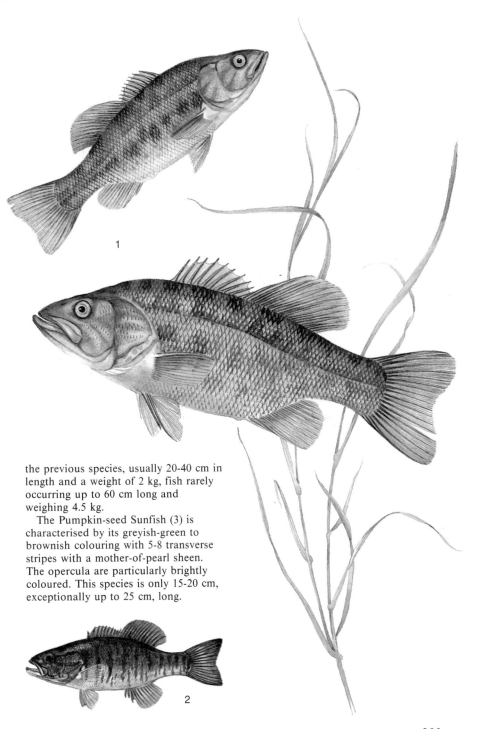

the previous species, usually 20-40 cm in
length and a weight of 2 kg, fish rarely
occurring up to 60 cm long and
weighing 4.5 kg.

The Pumpkin-seed Sunfish (3) is
characterised by its greyish-green to
brownish colouring with 5-8 transverse
stripes with a mother-of-pearl sheen.
The opercula are particularly brightly
coloured. This species is only 15-20 cm,
exceptionally up to 25 cm, long.

Miller's Thumb, Bullhead
Cottus gobio
Cottidae

The Miller's Thumb is distributed in Europe from the northern coast of Spain to the area feeding the Baltic Sea, in Italy, Dalmatia, in the Vardar and Danube rivers, in the Crimea and in the rivers Pechora, Dniestr and Prut. It inhabits mountain and submontane brooks and small rivers with cool, well-oxygenated water. The body, which is flattened on top, is adapted for life near the bottom of swift water. Irregular dark spots on the light greyish-green basic colouring create the impression of the contour of the body blending in smoothly with the background substrate on the bottom (2). This camouflage ensures the safety of the Miller's Thumb. As it does not have a swim bladder, its locomotion is restricted to jerky leaps. It spends most time in a hiding-place under stones, where it seeks refuge from the swift current, protection from enemies, and also its food. This consists of small bottom-dwelling fauna, mainly species living under stones. In the spawning period it enhances its diet with eggs and fry, including its own. Each individual has a permanent shelter under a stone, which it only leaves in the evening and night hours, when it sets out to hunt food. The Miller's Thumb is faithful to its shelter for many years. From April to June it makes use of spaces under stones for spawning. The male seeks out and carefully cleans a small cave, where the female then lays 100-500 eggs, usually on to the ceiling. Sometimes a male succeeds in obtaining other females for spawning.

The Miller's Thumb comprises a significant component in the diet of Salmonid fishes, chiefly trout. Fishermen use it as bait. It grows to a length of 12-14 cm and a weight of 80 g.

The conspicuous, massive head of the Miller's Thumb (1) is an adaptation to life in waters with a swift current. The growth of the head bones have provided an armour which protects the head organs from sand and gravel being washed along the riverbed during downpours of rain and the spring thaw. The eyes of the Miller's Thumb are moreover protected with goggles formed by two layers of cornea, between which there is a liquid. The skin of the Miller's Thumb is entirely smooth and scaleless. In the event of a direct threat, the Miller's Thumb positions itself face to face with its adversary, extends the gills and the massive pectoral fins and opens wide its broad, toothed mouth (3). The

204

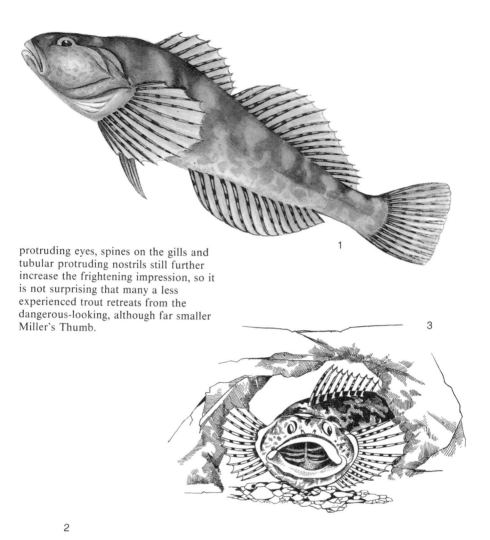

1

protruding eyes, spines on the gills and
tubular protruding nostrils still further
increase the frightening impression, so it
is not surprising that many a less
experienced trout retreats from the
dangerous-looking, although far smaller
Miller's Thumb.

3

2

Alpine Bullhead
Cottus poecilopus

Cottidae

The Alpine Bullhead inhabits mountain brooks and torrents of northern and central Europe, and Asia as far as the Kolyma river in Siberia, from the regions feeding the Oder and Danube rivers as far as the Amur.

Its mode of life is similar to that of the Miller's Thumb, although it requires a higher oxygen content in the water, therefore living in the more upstream reaches of rivers with a swifter current. It frequently ascends as far as spring source regions. At the margin between mountain waters and the submontane zone it occurs together with the Miller's Thumb. In these places the two species also reproduce together and cross-breeding often occurs. It seems that Alpine Bullhead is a more aggressive species, because in those places where it is in contact with the Miller's Thumb it is more numerous to a ratio of roughly 3:1.

On account of their pugnacious behaviour and large mouths, Bullheads were once considered to be seriously detrimental in trout waters. As food analyses have shown, however, their negative effect on Salmonid fishes was overestimated. The diet of the Bullhead consists predominantly of animals living under stones which are inaccessible to trout and the Charr. By hunting these, therefore, Bullheads make use of a food source which would go unused without them. Bullheads themselves often fall prey to large trout, thus being a rich source of proteins in cool mountain waters, which are otherwise quite poor in food.

The Alpine Bullhead (1) usually grows to a length of 15 cm at a weight of 80 g. The largest individuals measure up to 20 cm and live for up to 6 years. The body structure and colouring are similar to those of the Miller's Thumb, although the mouth is broader and the lateral line incomplete. On the upper edge of the front dorsal fin there is an orange border, which is particularly pronounced in males; these furthermore differ from the females by having larger and broader heads, longer fins and darker colouring.

The most pronounced distinguishing features between the Miller's Thumb and the Alpine Bullhead are found on the ventral side of the body. The Miller's Thumb (2) has one nerve pore in the centre of the chin. The ventral

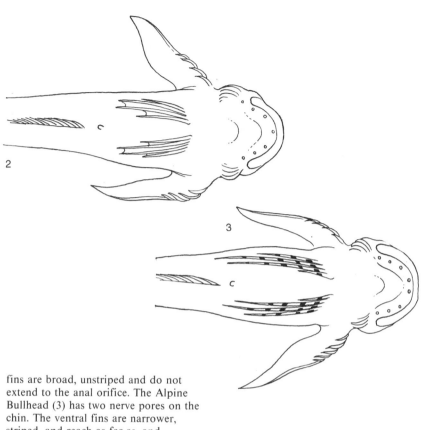

fins are broad, unstriped and do not
extend to the anal orifice. The Alpine
Bullhead (3) has two nerve pores on the
chin. The ventral fins are narrower,
striped, and reach as far as, and
sometimes even beyond, the anal orifice.

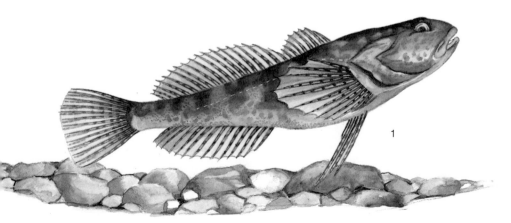

Fourhorn Sculpin, Fourhorn Bullhead
Myoxocephalus quadricornis
Cottidae

The shape of the body of the Fourhorn Sculpin betrays its relation-ship to freshwater bullheads of the genus *Cottus*. However, it grows to a greater size, usually 20-35 cm, and a weight of 150-200 g. On rare occasions specimens have been caught measuring around 60 cm. It occurs in the sea and brackish water along the Arctic coast of Europe, Asia and North America. It also occurs in the fresh water of Scandi-navian and Karelian lakes and in the Great Lakes in North America. In the above-mentioned lakes and in the Baltic Sea it is a relic from the Ice Age and lives on the rocky bottom of coasts with a growth of aquatic plants. The females are larger than the males. Spawning takes place from December to January. The female lays the 2,000-6,200 eggs on the bottom among stones and the male actively guards them. After the fry hatch, however, they often fall prey to their own parents. The usual diet consists of smaller fishes, their fry and crustaceans. Be-cause of its white tasty meat, this species is fished for from time to time, but it is of no particular economic importance.

The species *Benthophilus macrocephalus*, a member of the family Gobiidae, is only 5-10 cm long. It is distributed in the Caspian Sea and the Sea of Azov, from where it penetrates the lower reaches of rivers. It lives on small bottom invertebrates, mainly worms, molluscs, crustaceans and insect larvae. It is of no economic importance.

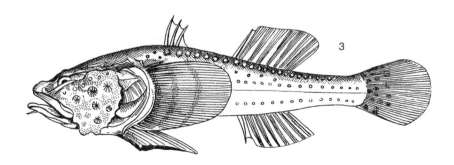

3

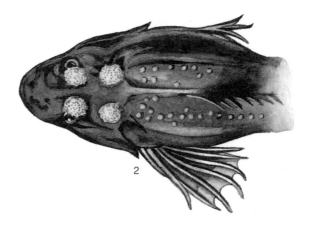

The four horny protuberances on each operculum have given the Fourhorn Sculpin (1) both its scientific and vernacular names. The body is foreshortened with a long, narrow peduncle behind. There are small bony platelets in the skin, forming 1-2 rows above the lateral line. Conspicuous features are two pairs of yellow, spongy protuberances behind the eyes and in the nape (2). The sexes can be distinguished by the length of the second dorsal fin; in males this is longer, and when laid against the body extends as far as the base of the caudal fin.

Benthophilus macrocephalus (3) has a flattened body with a massive head and two dorsal fins. The ventral fins are fused into a suction disc. There are bony platelets on the body in the skin.

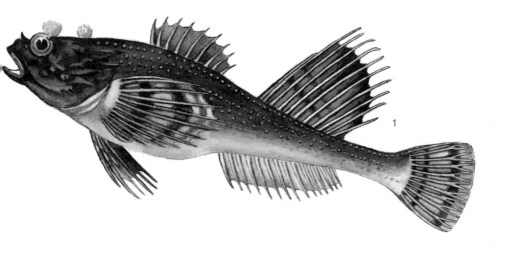

Mottled Black Sea Goby, Tubenose Goby
Proterorhinus marmoratus   Gobiidae

The Mottled Black Sea Goby inhabits brackish waters, rivers and lakes in the areas feeding the Black and Caspian Seas and the Sea of Azov. It inhabits the shallow water of the coast, from where it penetrates rivers (the Danube, the Araks, the Bug, the Dniestr and the Prut) and their tributaries, as well as lakes (the Neusiedler, the Balaton), and even drainage canals and the waters of flood zones. It lives near the bottom in places with mildly flowing water and sufficient hiding-places. As it has no swim bladder, it is a poor swimmer, moving with jerking leaps along the bottom. Despite its apparent clumsiness, however, it is able, when disturbed, to disappear at lightning speed into a hiding-place under stones, bankside roots or aquatic growth, where it also conceals itself during the day. It does not swim out for food until after dark. It lives on small insect larvae, worms and molluscs and grows to a length of only 7-10, rarely up to 12 cm.

Depending on the water temperature, it spawns from March to May. The elongated eggs are stuck by the female into bowl-shaped nests constructed in the bottom. Apart from the nests, females make use of various objects for the deposit of eggs, such as mollusc shells, suitably shaped stones, and even drainage pipes, cans or glass containers. The female lays up to 2,500 eggs, which are guarded by one of the parents. The male differs from the female by having a longer and more pointed urogenital papilla, although this difference is scarcely distinguishable in smaller individuals outside the breeding season. They begin spawning at an age of 2-3 years, the majority perishing after the first spawning. Only rarely do these fish live up to 5 years.

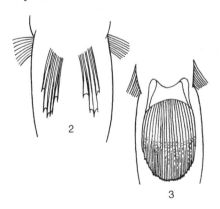

The Mottled Black Sea Goby (1) is adapted both in its body shape and colouring to life at the bottom. It has a spindle-shaped, flat-sided body with inconspicuous yellowish-brown, darkly mottled colouring. A striking feature are the tubular nostrils suspended above the upper lip. It is similar to bullheads both in its body shape and colouring. The most striking distinguishing features are the free ventral fins of bullheads (2). In the Mottled Black Sea Goby the ventral fins are fused into a suction disc (3), with which it attaches itself to the bottom in order to withstand the dashing of waves; the original habitat of fishes of the family Gobiidae was the wave breaking zone of the coast. Differences in the body covering are less conspicuous. Whereas the body of the Mottled Black Sea Goby is covered with small, rough scales and the lateral line is absent, bullheads have unscaled bodies with scaly formations along the lateral line only.

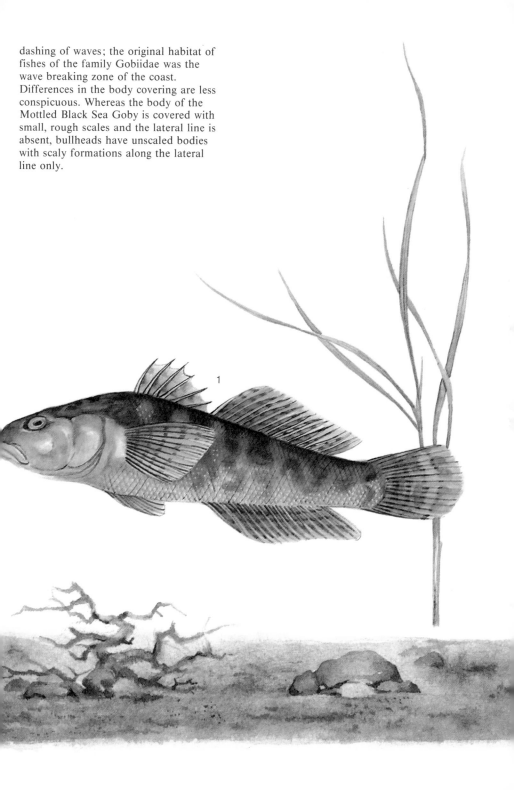

Canestrini's Goby
Pomatoschistus canestrini   Gobiidae

Fishes of the genus *Pomatoschistus* rank among the smallest representatives of the family Gobiidae. As they never even reach a length of
10 cm, they escape attention in nature. Their small size is also the reason for their lack of economic importance, interest in studying them
therefore being absent. Consequently little is known about the life of
fishes of the genus *Pomatoschistus*.

Canestrini's Goby is a freshwater representative of the genus, living
in isolated populations, both in Croatia in the river Jadro not far from
Split, and in Italy around Venice. It lives on small invertebrates, mainly
crustaceans and insect larvae.

The Common Goby (*Pomatoschistus microps*) is a predominantly
sea species, occurring in shallow water along the coast of Europe
from Norway as far as the Mediterranean and Black Seas and the Sea
of Azov. It often swims into the brackish waters of estuaries. It
spawns in pairs up to eight times in the period from April to September. The male finds a suitable shell or stone, cleans its surface, and
the female then lays the 500-1,000 eggs on to the chosen base. The
male takes care of them, guarding both the eggs and the hatched fry.
Young fish mature within as little as a year, and few individuals live
longer than 2 years. They live on small invertebrate fauna of the bottom, mainly crustaceans.

Canestrini's Goby (1) grows to
a maximum length of 6 cm, the males
being about a third smaller than the
females. Characteristic features are the
two dorsal fins, the ventral fins, which
are fused into a sucker, and the
symmetrical, convex caudal fin. Apart
from their smaller size, males also differ
in having six dark, indistinct stripes
across the sides.

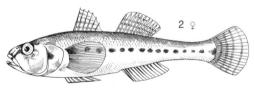

In contrast with the preceding species, the male of the Common Goby (2) has about 12 transverse stripes on the sides of the body. The female has a row of dark spots along the lateral line. The species grows to a length of only 3-5 cm, in isolated cases up to 8 cm. Males are about a third smaller than females.

1

Panizza's Goby
Padogobius panizzai

Gobiidae

Panizza's Goby lives exclusively in northern Italy, in rivers near Venice, for example in the Po, and in lakes Garda and Maggiore. Little is known about its reproduction, except that it spawns on the bottom of sandy and stony places. It eats small invertebrates of the bottom. It grows to a length of 3-5, rarely up to 6 cm.

The Caspian Goby (*Caspiosoma caspium*) ranks among the smallest European fish species, growing to a length of 3-4, exceptionally up to 5 cm. It does not differ from the preceding species either in the shape of its body or the position of the fins. It inhabits the northern regions of the Caspian and Black Seas and the Sea of Azov. It keeps to the lower reaches of large rivers such as the Volga, Don and Dnieper, and in the brackish waters of their estuaries. Its diet consists of invertebrates, mainly small crustaceans, and insect larvae in fresh water. Its biology is not known in any great detail.

The Racer Goby (*Gobius gymnotrachelus*), occurs in several brooks and lakes in the northern part of the area feeding the Black Sea, in the brackish water of the northern coast of the Black Sea, and along the whole coast of the Caspian Sea. It spawns in pairs in April and May in a previously prepared nest in the bottom. The eggs are guarded by the male. The diet consists predominantly of crustaceans. It is of local significance for fishing in the Black Sea.

Another goby species living in brackish and fresh waters is the Toad Goby (*Gobius batrachocephalus*), which occurs in the areas feeding the Black Sea and the Sea of Azov. It grows to a larger size, therefore being a significant species for Black Sea fishing.

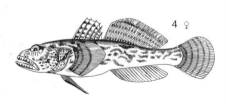

4 ♀

Panizza's Goby (1) has a cylindrical body with two dorsal fins. The ventral fins are fused into a sucker. A conspicuous feature is the high position of the eyes. The male differs from the female in the inconspicuous dark brown spots on the last two vanes of the first dorsal fin, and in the greater number of dark transverse stripes, linked by oblique lines at the level of the lateral line.

The Caspian Goby (2) has a pointed pectoral fin, smooth scaleless skin, large irregular dark spots on the body and stripes on the head.

The female of the Racer Goby (3) has a light colouring with dark spots. The male is smaller and black in colour.

The female of the Toad Goby (4) grows to a length of up to 35 cm, females being a third smaller and black in colour.

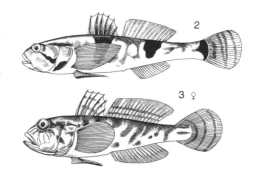

River Blenny
Blennius fluviatilis

Blenniidae

The River Blenny is the only representative of the family Blenniidae that lives in fresh water. It is distributed in brooks, rivers and lakes of the north and north-western area feeding the Mediterranean Sea. It prefers clear water with a stony bottom. Adult fish live solitarily in hiding-places under stones or roots. As the River Blenny does not have a swim bladder, it is not able to swim in open water, moving by leaps at the level of the bottom. When it lies on stones it rests on the reduced and fused hard rays of the ventral fins.

The male is a pronounced brownish-black during the breeding season. He defends suitable places under roots, stones or the bank, to where it entices the female. The male fertilises the eggs and actively guards them. By means of the pectoral fins, he fans fresh, oxygen-enriched water and removes unfertilised and damaged eggs. During this period he does not feed. The female, on the other hand, does not take care of the young, feeding herself intensively. The fry hatch after 14 days at a temperature of 20 °C. They gather in great shoals, seeking food in shallows near the bank. At first they feed on plankton, later on small bottom-dwelling invertebrates, mainly crustaceans.

The River Blenny is of no economic significance. Anglers use it as bait. It also serves as food for predatory fishes.

The River Blenny (1) has a small, elongate body with long dorsal and anal fins. Its naked, scaleless body is protected by a thick layer of mucus. The dorsal fin is without indentation and the spiny section is joined directly to the soft-rayed section. The back is a lead brown, the sides lighter and the belly yellowish-white. The whole body is covered with brownish-green, rounded or elongated spots. Both sexes have small branched processes above the eyes, males moreover also having an adipose ridge on the crown of the head which increases in size with age.

The size of the River Blenny ranges from 8 to 12 cm, rarely up to 15 cm. The relatively large teeth on both jaws betray the fact that this is a predatory fish species.

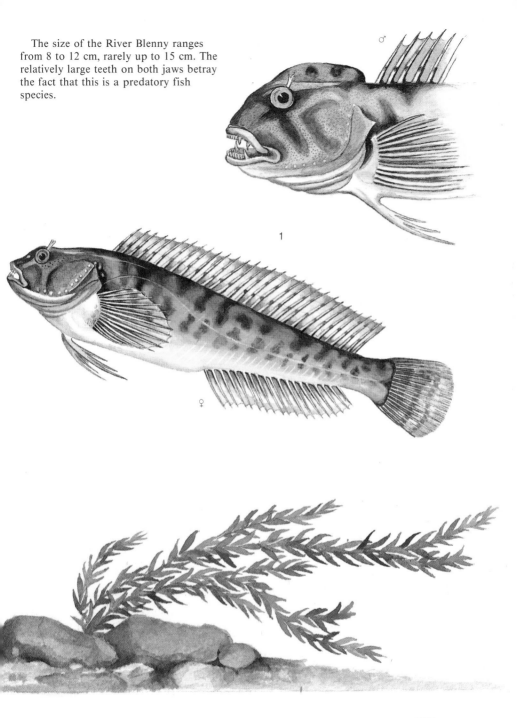

1

Flounder
Platichthys flesus

The Flounder lives along the coast of Europe from the Arctic Ocean as far as the Mediterranean and Black Seas and the Sea of Azov. It is a pelagic, coastal fish, which likes to enter fresh waters, sometimes penetrating far upstream. It has an asymmetrical, flat-sided body. Adult Flounder lie on their left side, although about one third of these fish lie on the right side. It swims by undulating the dorsal and anal fins. The body is covered with star-shaped bony platelets and two types of scales. On the body there are ctenoid scales, and on the peduncle cycloid scales. It spawns from February to May on the seabed at depths of 20-40 m. As in most flatfishes, the eggs are pelagic. The fry swim into brackish and fresh river waters, staying there until they mature. At first they feed on small crustaceans, later on small bottom fauna. The Flounder usually attains a length of 20-30 cm, in rare cases up to 50 cm, and a weight of 4 kg. It lives for a maximum of 16 years. It is an economically important species, the overall annual catch in European waters totalling 10,000 tons.

The Dover Sole (*Solea solea*) is a pelagic, coastal species, here and there penetrating fresh waters. Its body is leaf-like to tongue-like in shape. It inhabits the coasts of western and southern Europe from the North Sea to the Mediterranean Sea, where it lives on sands at depths from 10 to 100 m. In the estuaries of large rivers, it keeps to muddy deposits. It normally grows to a length of 30-40 cm and 1-2 kg in weight, rarely up to 60 cm and 3 kg. It is a significant species for fishing, annual catches ranging from 35,000 to 45,000 tons.

The Flounder (1) has an asymmetrical, flat-sided body. It lies on one side, the other side forming the back of the body. Both the embryos in the eggs and the freshly hatched fry are symmetrical (2).

4

218

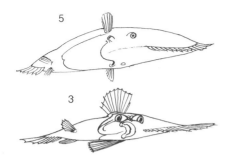

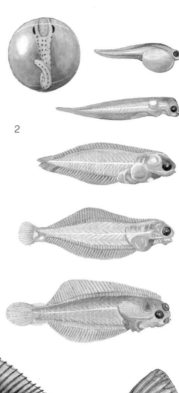

the eyes, do not shift. The eyes are small, since the senses used in hunting food are smell and touch, for which the mouth processes on the lower side of the head are important.

The fry live pelagically for about 50 days, and when reaching the length of 11 mm lose their symmetry. During its development, the young Flounder (3) loses the swim bladder, the whole head turning and the mouth shifting to one side, the eye moving across the front edge of the head to the right and finishing next to the other eye.

In fishes of the family Soleidae, a representative of which is the Dover Sole (4), the formation of the head (5) is different. The dorsal fin reaches almost as far as the snout. The nostrils, unlike

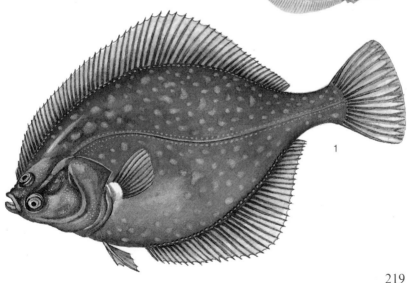

219

INDEX

Numbers in bold refer to main entries, numbers in italics to illustrations

220

221